REVISION NOTES FOR
ADVANCED LEVEL INORGANIC CHEMISTRY

By the same authors

REVISION NOTES FOR ADVANCED LEVEL PHYSICAL CHEMISTRY
TEST GRIDS FOR ORDINARY LEVEL CHEMISTRY
TEST GRIDS FOR ADVANCED LEVEL CHEMISTRY
NEW CALCULATIONS IN CHEMISTRY FOR O LEVEL
INORGANIC REACTIONS AT ADVANCED LEVEL
ORGANIC REACTIONS AT ADVANCED LEVEL
EXPERIMENTAL PHYSICAL CHEMISTRY

REVISION NOTES
FOR ADVANCED LEVEL
INORGANIC
CHEMISTRY

by

D. G. DAVIES, B.Sc., A.R.I.C.
Head of the Science Department, Palmer's College

T. V. G. KELLY, B.Sc.
Head of the Chemistry Department, William Ellis School

ALLMAN & SON LIMITED

First published 1969 by Allman & Son Ltd
17–19 Foley Street, London W1A 1DR

© 1969 D. G. Davies and T. V. G. Kelly

Second edition 1974

ISBN 0·204·79359·9

Made and printed in Great Britain by
William Clowes & Sons, Limited, London, Beccles and Colchester

PREFACE

We have written these notes to help the student at 'A' level to organise the large body of inorganic facts which he is still required to recall for the purpose of examination. The facts themselves (and this usually means reactions) have been grouped in the form of flowsheets; most students find these useful because they enable the salient points of the chemistry of an element or compound to be seen at a glance.

The physical basis of inorganic chemistry is emphasised throughout and references are made to the companion volume to this book, *Revision Notes for Advanced Level Physical Chemistry*.

D.G.D.
T.K.

1969

NOTE ON 1974 EDITION

The nomenclature of chemical compounds in this edition is generally consistent with that used by most Examination Boards and is based on the IUPAC system. Exceptions are where commercially important compounds are unlikely to be recognised by other than their 'traditional' names.

1974

D.G.D.
T.K.

CONTENTS

Chapter   Page

1   THE PERIODIC CLASSIFICATION OF THE ELEMENTS   1

2   THE ELECTROCHEMICAL SERIES   9

3   TYPES OF SUBSTANCE AND TYPES OF REACTION   12

4   GROUP COMPARISONS AND ELEMENT FLOW-SHEETS
     Section A   Hydrogen   34
     Section B   Group I   38
     Section C   Group II   42
     Section D   Group III   46
     Section E   Group IV   50
     Section F   Group V   58
     Section G   Group VI   66
     Section H   Group VII   75

5   THE NOBLE GASES   82

6   THE TRANSITION ELEMENTS   85

7   THE EXTRACTION OF ELEMENTS
     Section A   The metals   96
     Section B   The non-metals   112

8   THE MANUFACTURE OF SOME COMMERCIALLY IMPORTANT COMPOUNDS   121

9   INDEX   133

ATOMIC NUMBER	ELEMENT	SYMBOL	MAIN ENERGY LEVELS OF ELECTRONS ('SHELLS')			
			1	*2*	*3*	*4*
1	Hydrogen	H	1			
2	**Helium**	**He**	**2**			
3	Lithium	Li	2	1		
4	Beryllium	Be	2	2		
5	Boron	B	2	3		
6	Carbon	C	2	4		
7	Nitrogen	N	2	5		
8	Oxygen	O	2	6		
9	Fluorine	F	2	7		
10	**Neon**	**Ne**	**2**	**8**		
11	Sodium	Na	2	8	1	
12	Magnesium	Mg	2	8	2	
13	Aluminium	Al	2	8	3	
14	Silicon	Si	2	8	4	
15	Phosphorus	P	2	8	5	
16	Sulphur	S	2	8	6	
17	Chlorine	Cl	2	8	7	
18	**Argon**	**Ar**	**2**	**8**	**8**	
19	Potassium	K	2	8	8	1
20	Calcium	Ca	2	8	8	2
21	Scandium	Sc	2	8	9	2
22	Titanium	Ti	2	8	10	2
23	Vanadium	V	2	8	11	2
24	Chromium	Cr	2	8	13	1
25	Manganese	Mn	2	8	13	2
26	Iron	Fe	2	8	14	2
27	Cobalt	Co	2	8	15	2
28	Nickel	Ni	2	8	16	2
29	Copper	Cu	2	8	18	1
30	Zinc	Zn	2	8	18	2
31	Gallium	Ga	2	8	18	3
32	Germanium	Ge	2	8	18	4
33	Arsenic	As	2	8	18	5
34	Selenium	Se	2	8	18	6
35	Bromine	Br	2	8	18	7
36	**Krypton**	**Kr**	**2**	**8**	**18**	**8**

Chapter 1

The Periodic Classification of the Elements

An examination of the table of electronic configurations on the opposite page reveals a periodic recurrence of elements with similar numbers of electrons in their outer shells, e.g. F, Cl and Br (and also I, which is not shown); all have seven outer electrons. Elements with similar outer electronic configurations have similar chemical (and frequently physical) properties since it is the outer electrons which are involved during chemical reactions.

STRUCTURE OF THE PERIODIC TABLE

If the elements are arranged in a table in order of atomic number such that elements with similar outer configurations (and therefore properties) fall in vertical columns, the result is as shown on p. 2. This table is called the *Periodic Table* or *Periodic Classification* of the elements.

The columns are called **groups** and the rows **periods**. Each period begins with an alkali metal (H, in the first period, is an exception) and ends with a noble gas. In the first three periods (short periods) electrons are added only to the outer shell, as one passes across the table, and there is a fairly marked change in properties from one element to the next, e.g.

Na	Mg	Al	Si	P	S	Cl	Ar
v. soft, highly reactive metal	brittle, reactive metal	soft metal; some non-metal character	fairly inert non-metal	moderately reactive non-metal	very reactive non-metal	highly reactive, gaseous non-metal	noble gas; non-metal

In the next three periods (long periods) electrons are added to the outer shell only for the first two and last six elements as one passes across the table; the intermediate elements are built up by electrons filling an inner shell while the outer shell remains constant (with a few exceptions, e.g. Cu) at 2, e.g. period 4.

The Periodic Classification.

Non-transition groups		Transition groups									Non-transition groups					
I	II	iii	iv	v	vi	vii	viii			i	ii	III	IV	V	VI	VII	0
's' block		'd' block										'p' block					
H 1																H 1	He 2
Li 3	Be 4											B 5	C 6	N 7	O 8	F 9	Ne 10
Na 11	Mg 12											Al 13	Si 14	P 15	S 16	Cl 17	Ar 18
K 19	Ca 20	Sc 21	Ti 22	V 23	Cr 24	Mn 25	Fe 26	Co 27	Ni 28	Cu 29	Zn 30	Ga 31	Ge 32	As 33	Se 34	Br 35	Kr 36
Rb 37	Sr 38	Y 39	Zr 40	Nb 41	Mo 42	Tc 43	Ru 44	Rh 45	Pd 46	Ag 47	Cd 48	In 49	Sn 50	Sb 51	Te 52	I 53	Xe 54
Cs 55	Ba 56	La* 57	Hf 72	Ta 73	W 74	Re 75	Os 76	Ir 77	Pt 78	Au 79	Hg 80	Tl 81	Pb 82	Bi 83	Po 84	At 85	Rn 86
Fr 87	Ra 88	Ac** 89															

'f' block

Lanthanides

*	Ce 58	Pr 59	Nd 60	Pm 61	Sm 62	Eu 63	Gd 64	Tb 65	Dy 66	Ho 67	Er 68	Tm 69	Yb 70	Lu 71

Actinides

**	Th 90	Pa 91	U 92	Np 93	Pu 94	Am 95	Cm 96	Bk 97	Cf 98	Ei 99	Fm 100	Md 101	No 102	Lw 103

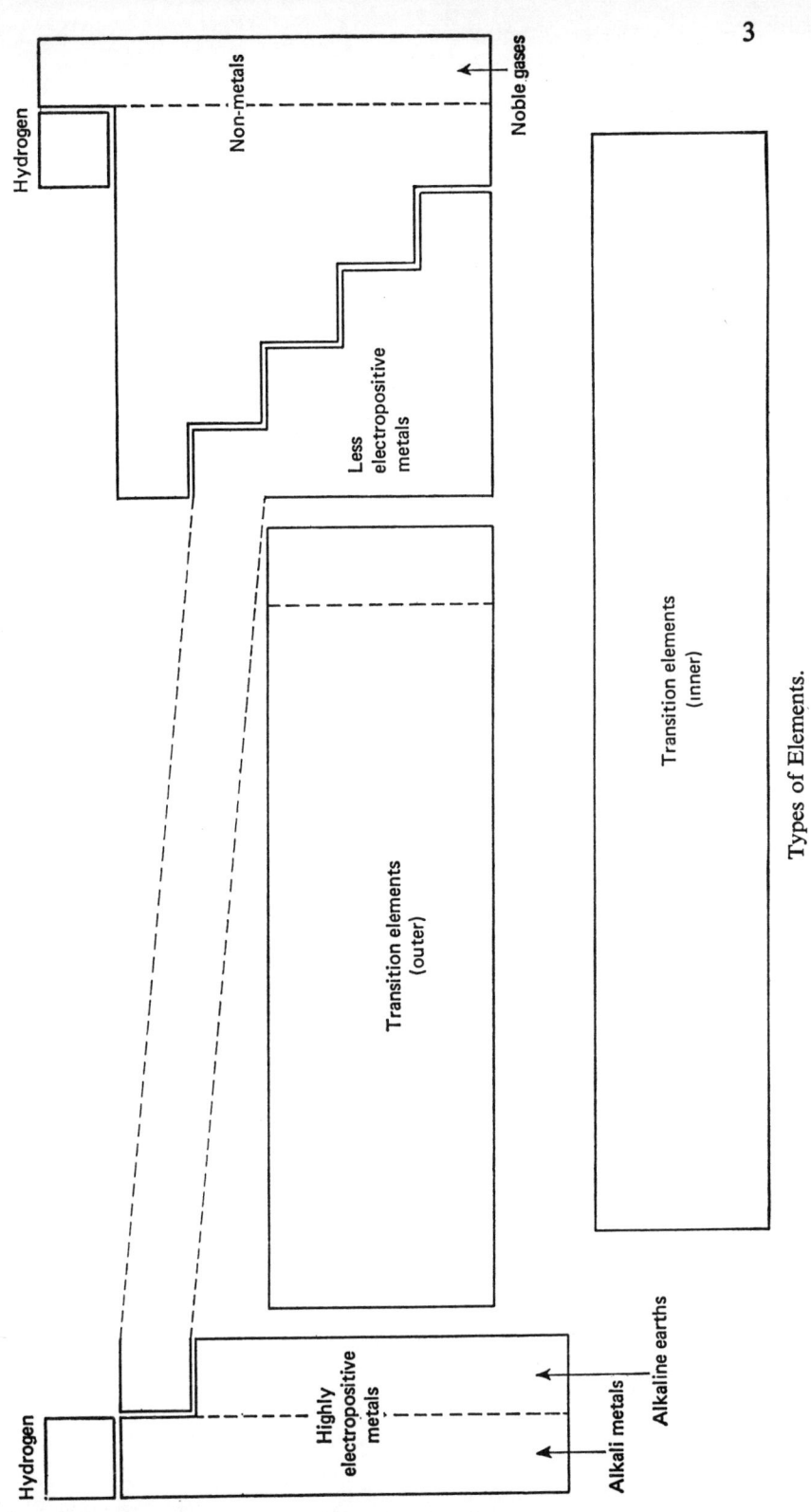

Types of Elements.

K	Ca	Sc Ti V Cr Mn Fe Co Ni Cu Zn	Ga	Ge	As Se	Br	Kr
		transition elements					
v. soft, highly reactive metal	brittle, very reactive metal	Majority are tough, moderately reactive metals exhibiting multiple valency and forming coloured hydrated ions. Alloy readily.	soft metal, some non-metallic character	metal-loid	fairly reactive non-metals	very reactive, liquid non-metal	noble gas
outer shell being filled		inner shell being filled			outer shell being filled		

These intermediate elements (all contained within the centre block of the Periodic Table) are called *transition elements*; they are dealt with in Chapter 6. Only gradual changes in properties are noticeable in passing through a **transition series.**

SOME USEFUL GENERALISATIONS

Types of element

The table on p. 3 shows how the elements may be divided into four main classes—(a) strongly electropositive metals, (b) transition metals, (c) weakly electropositive metals (and metalloids) and (d) non-metals. Classes (a) (b) and (d) may be usefully subdivided as shown in the table.

Weakly electropositive metals are considered to be those which do not readily form simple positive ions and, though they are predominantly metallic, exhibit some non-metallic characteristics, e.g. may have amphoteric oxides. They frequently exhibit covalence, e.g. Sn in $SnCl_4$.

Comparative reactivity and types of bonding

Ion formation and high reactivity are favoured by
- (a) (i) increasing atomic radius—for positive ions (electrons more readily lost),
  - (ii) decreasing atomic radius—for negative ions (electrons more readily captured);
- (b) a small number of electrons (1 or 2, and very occasionally 3) to be lost or gained to give a noble gas (or other stable) configuration.

Where contrary conditions operate covalent bonding tends to predominate.

The following diagrams summarise the above in relation to the positions of the elements in the Periodic Table. The transition metals and the noble gases are not included.

Comparative Atomic Radii.

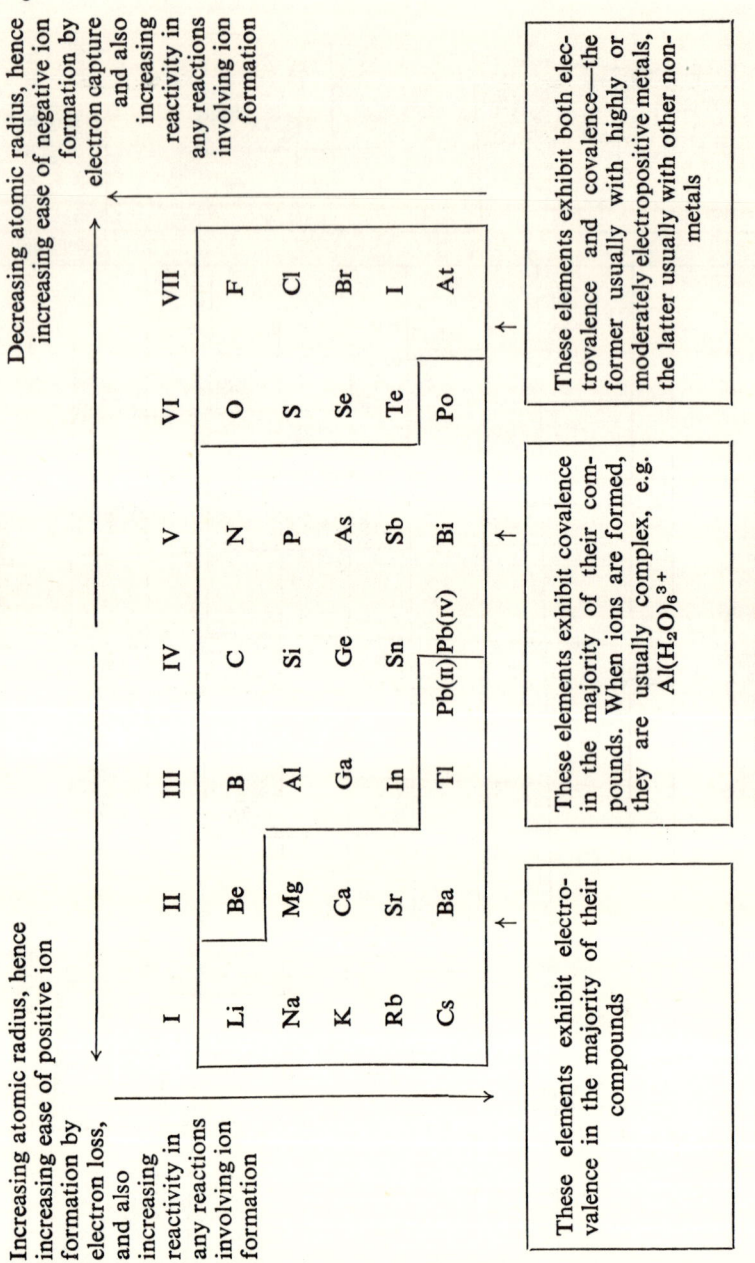

Increasing atomic radius, hence increasing ease of positive ion formation by electron loss, and also increasing reactivity in any reactions involving ion formation

Decreasing atomic radius, hence increasing ease of negative ion formation by electron capture and also increasing reactivity in any reactions involving ion formation

I	II	III	IV	V	VI	VII
Li	Be	B	C	N	O	F
Na	Mg	Al	Si	P	S	Cl
K	Ca	Ga	Ge	As	Se	Br
Rb	Sr	In	Sn	Sb	Te	I
Cs	Ba	Tl	Pb(II) Pb(IV)	Bi	Po	At

These elements exhibit electrovalence in the majority of their compounds

These elements exhibit covalence in the majority of their compounds. When ions are formed, they are usually complex, e.g. $Al(H_2O)_6^{3+}$

These elements exhibit both electrovalence and covalence—the former usually with highly or moderately electropositive metals, the latter usually with other non-metals

Reactivity and types of bonding.

A COMPARISON OF THE OXIDES, CHLORIDES AND HYDRIDES OF THE
ELEMENTS OF THE THIRD PERIOD

In passing across the Periodic Table oxides of elements change
from basic (and ionic) to acidic (and covalent). These and
other changes are summarised in the table on p. 8. Similar
changes may be observed in compounds of the non-transition
elements of the long periods.

DIAGONAL RELATIONSHIPS

The first member of Group I, lithium, has in many ways more
in common with magnesium (the second member of Group II)
than with other elements in Group I. This type of **diagonal
relationship** is also seen with

$$\text{Be (Group II)—Al (Group III)}$$
and $$\text{B (Group III)—Si (Group IV)}$$

This phenomenon is largely due to the very small atomic
radii of Li (etc.) in comparison with Na (etc.) and the consequent lesser tendency to lose electrons.

GROUP	I	II	III	IV	V	VI	VII	0
ELEMENT	Na	Mg	Al	Si	P	S	Cl	Ar
Electronic Configuration	2, 8, 1	2, 8, 2	2, 8, 3	2, 8, 4	2, 8, 5	2, 8, 6	2, 8, 7	2, 8, 8
Max. valency = Gp. No.	1	2	3	4	5	6	7	0
Min. valency (Gps. V, VI and VII) = 8 – Gp. No.					3	2	1	0
Oxide	Na_2O	MgO	Al_2O_3	$(SiO_2)_n$ polymer	P_4O_6 P_4O_{10}	SO_2 SO_3	Cl_2O Cl_2O_7 and others	
properties	basic		amphoteric	acidic				
bonding	ionic			covalent				
Chloride bonding	NaCl	$MgCl_2$ ionic solids	Al_2Cl_6 solid ionic; melt and vapour co-valent	$SiCl_4$	PCl_3 covalent liquids PCl_5 vapour covalent, solid is $PCl_4^+ PCl_6^-$	S_2Cl_2		
degree of hydrolysis	nil	slight	extensive	complete				
Hydride	NaH	Does not exist but CaH_2, SrH_2 and BaH_2 do.	AlH_3	SiH_4	PH_3	H_2S	HCl	
bonding	ionic solids		covalent, very unstable	covalent gases				
properties	salts			neutral	weakly basic	weakly acidic	strongly acidic	
degree of hydrolysis	complete				virtually unaffected	slight acid ionisation	almost complete acid ionisation	

A comparison of the oxides, chlorides and hydrides of the elements of the third period.

Chapter 2

The Electrochemical Series

STANDARD ELECTRODE POTENTIAL
When a metal is placed in an aqueous solution of its ions a p.d. is set up between the metal and the solution. This results from the equilibrium established between two opposing processes— (a) the tendency of the metal to pass into solution as ions, (b) the tendency of the ions to deposit as metal, i.e.

$$M \rightleftharpoons M^{n+} + ne$$

When the solution is molar (or, more accurately, of unit activity) with respect to the ions the p.d. is called the **standard electrode potential** of the metal. (For a fuller treatment see p. 89 of *Revision Notes for Advanced Level Physical Chemistry*.)

REACTIVITY SERIES
The greater the tendency of a metal to form ions the greater is the p.d. between the metal and the solution of its ions. Thus if metals are placed in order of their standard electrode potentials they will also be in the order in which they tend to form ions, i.e. their order of reactivity. This arrangement of metals is known as the **electrochemical series**.

K Ba Ca Na Mg Al Mn Zn Fe Ni Sn Pb (H) Cu Hg Ag Au
$$\longrightarrow$$
decreasing tendency to form ions

THE BEHAVIOUR OF METALS IN RELATION TO THEIR POSITIONS IN THE ELECTROCHEMICAL SERIES
The main trends (as the series is descended K → Au) are

9

(1) Reducing power, i.e. the tendency to donate electrons, decreases. Metals reduce the compounds of other metals which occur below them, e.g.

$$6Na + Al_2Cl_6 \longrightarrow 2Al + 6NaCl$$
$$2Al + Fe_2O_3 \longrightarrow 2Fe + Al_2O_3$$

Other familiar examples are

(a) displacement of metals from solutions of their salts
$$Zn + Cu^{2+} \longrightarrow Zn^{2+} + Cu$$

and (b) displacement of hydrogen from aqueous solutions of non-oxidising acids (e.g. HCl, HBr, dil. H_2SO_4) only by metals above H in the E.C.S.

(2) During electrolysis the ions of a metal are more likely to be discharged the lower it is in the series, e.g. during the electrolysis of aqueous copper(II) sulphate (cations present Cu^{2+}, H^+) the Cu^{2+} ions are discharged in preference to the H^+ ions; Na^+ ions are discharged in preference to Ca^{2+} ions during the extraction of sodium (p. 41).

(3) The vigour of reaction with reagents such as water and acids decreases.

(4) All the metals down as far as Ag react with oxidising acids (HNO_3, conc. H_2SO_4), but the higher the metal in the series the more extensive the reduction of the acid, e.g.

$$\text{conc. } H_2SO_4 \text{ with Zn} \longrightarrow SO_2, S, H_2S$$
$$\text{with Cu} \longrightarrow SO_2 \text{ only}$$

$$HNO_3 \text{ with Zn} \longrightarrow NO_2, NO, N_2O \text{ and } NH_3$$
$$\text{with Cu} \longrightarrow NO_2 \text{ and NO only}$$

(5) The properties of some compounds of the metals are related to the positions of the metals in the E.C.S. This applies particularly to thermal stability (which decreases considerably) and to some extent to solubility, the more soluble compounds usually being those of metals higher in the series.

The table on p. 11 summarises some of these trends.

Au	Ag	Hg	Cu	(H)	Pb	Sn	Ni	Fe	Zn	Mn	Al	Mg	Na	Ca	Ba	K

Property	Description (Au → K)
Standard electrode potential	increasingly positive ← arbitrary zero (Standard) [at (H)] → increasingly negative
Extraction of metal	Various methods; easy reduction of compounds | by autoreduction | by external reducing agent | by electrolysis (Mg also thermally)
Action on water	no action | decompose steam on heating | rapidly decompose cold water
Action on HCl and dil. H_2SO_4	no action | hydrogen displaced, e.g. $Fe + 2H^+ \longrightarrow Fe^{2+} + H_2$
Action on HNO_3 and conc. H_2SO_4	gold not attacked | attacked; extent of reduction of reagent decreasing ←
H_2 on heated oxide	reduction to the metal | not reduced to the metal
Thermal stability of compounds (general)	thermal stability of most compounds decreases ←
Thermal stability of oxide	unstable; yield metal and O_2 | generally stable; higher oxides, e.g. PbO_2, yield a lower oxide (stable) and O_2
Solubility and thermal stability of hydroxide	highly unstable; yielding oxide and water | sparingly soluble; stable at room temperature, lose water on gentle to moderate heating | water soluble, i.e. alkalis; stable
Solubility of sulphides	sparingly soluble in water; insoluble in dil. HCl | sparingly soluble in water; soluble in dil. HCl | extensively hydrolysed | soluble in water and hydrolysed

Chapter 3

Types of Substance and Types of Reaction

In classifying substances the principal criteria are the types of reactions in which they participate, so types of substance and types of reaction will be dealt with together as far as possible.

A CLASSIFICATION OF SUBSTANCES

The main body of common inorganic substances may be divided and subdivided as follows

- **(A) Elements:** (1) metals, (2) non-metals, (3) metalloids. (A more detailed classification of the elements is considered in Chapter 1)
- **(B) Compounds:** (1) acids, (2) bases, (3) oxides and hydroxides, (4) salts, (5) oxidising agents, (6) reducing agents, (7) acid chlorides, (8) covalent chlorides

A CLASSIFICATION OF REACTIONS

The majority of reactions may be grouped as follows

- (A) Acid–base
- (B) Redox (including displacement and disproportionation)
- (C) Dissociation and decomposition
- (D) Double decomposition
- (E) Hydrolysis, hydration and dehydration

There is no hard and fast rule about the above classifications and others will be found. In addition, many substances can behave in several of the above ways and so may be placed in more than one subdivision.

ELEMENTS

The majority of elements may be described as either metallic or non-metallic, but a few, e.g. As, Ge, show characteristics of both and are frequently called 'metalloids'.
The principal differences between metals and non-metals are summarised in the following table.

	Metals	Non-metals
Physical appearance	Lustrous solids (except Hg); ductile; malleable; good thermal conductors	Brittle, crystalline or powdery solids; many gaseous; poor thermal conductors
Structure of lattice	Ionic with 3-dimensional extension in 'sea' of electrons ⊕ e ⊕ e ⊕ e ⊕ / e ⊕ e ⊕ e ⊕ e / ⊕ e ⊕ e ⊕ e ⊕	Covalent; crystalline solids are either giant molecules (e.g. C, Si) or close packed discrete molecules (e.g. S_8 rings); gases (other than noble gases) have diatomic molecules
Allotropy (*see notes below*)	Less tendency to allotropy than non-metals; a common example is tin	Often exhibited, e.g. C, S, P, O
Electrical properties	Very good conductors; electrons move freely under p.d.	Insulators (except graphite); no free electrons
Ion formation	Form +ve ions by electron loss (oxidation—p. 25)	Form −ve ions by electron gain (reduction—p. 26)
Oxides	Lower oxides basic or amphoteric; higher oxides sometimes acidic, e.g. CrO_3	Acidic or neutral

[Table continued overleaf

	Metals	Non-metals
Hydroxy compounds	Hydroxides; predominantly ionic; basic or amphoteric	Oxyacids, e.g. $P(OH)_3$ or H_3PO_3; covalent
Chlorides	Mostly ionic solids; little or not hydrolysed by water	Covalent liquids (PCl_5 exception); completely hydrolysed (CCl_4 exception) to HCl and oxyacid
Hydrides	Stable hydrides are formed only by highly electropositive metals (e.g. ionic Na^+H^-); others very unstable when formed	Covalent gases or volatile liquids; many formed; stable
Oxyacid compounds	Readily form oxyacid salts, e.g. nitrates, carbonates; some give oxyacids (in soln.) in higher oxidation states, e.g. $HMnO_4$, H_2CrO_4	Give rise to the majority of oxyacids; do not form cations of salts
Reaction with conc. HNO_3	Form nitrates (Sn forms SnO_2,xH_2O); some rendered passive, e.g. Al, Fe, Cr	Forms highest oxyacid, or highest oxide if acid unstable, e.g. $S \rightarrow H_2SO_4$, $C \rightarrow CO_2$
Reactions with non-oxidising acids, e.g. HCl	Hydrogen evolved and salt formed if metal above H in electrochemical series	No reaction

Allotropy

An element which can exist in more than one structural form in the same physical state is said to exhibit *allotropy* (polymorphism as applied to elements).

There are two types of allotropy:

(i) *enantiotropic*—in which each structure (allotrope) is stable over a certain temperature range (e.g. S, see p. 68; Sn, see p. 51).

(ii) *monotropic*—in which there is only one stable allotrope; all others are metastable and revert to the stable form under all conditions (e.g. P, see p. 59).

COMPOUNDS

ACIDS

An acid may be defined as a compound which dissociates to give, amongst others, hydrogen ions.

In aqueous solution 'hydrogen ions' exist largely as hydrated protons, and the hydroxonium ion (H_3O^+) is one example of the possible species. The (covalent) acid molecule reacts with a water molecule to form a hydroxonium ion

$$HX + H_2O \rightleftharpoons H_3O^+ + X^-$$

but, for the sake of simplicity, the hydrogen ion is usually written as H^+, and the equation for the dissociation of an acid as

$$HX \rightleftharpoons H^+ + X^-$$

Strength of an acid

By the strength of an acid is meant the readiness with which it ionises in solution. If it ionises readily (i.e. the above equilibrium lies almost completely to the right without extreme dilution) it is said to be strong. Acids which do not give high concentrations of ions in solution, and which require extreme dilution before ionisation is complete, are said to be weak.

In water the common strong acids are HCl, HBr, HI, HNO_3, H_2SO_4. The vast majority of acids are weak, e.g. H_2SO_3, HNO_2, H_2S, CH_3COOH.

Basicity of an acid

The basicity of an acid is the number of hydrogen ions which may be formed from one molecule of the acid.

With di- and tribasic acids each succeeding ionisation is weaker than the previous one (see p. 58 of *Revision Notes for Advanced Level Physical Chemistry*).

BASES AND ACID-BASE REACTIONS

A base may be defined as a compound (or ion species) which combines with hydrogen ions, i.e. a proton acceptor.

The essential requirement for a compound to act as a base is the possession of a lone pair of electrons which can co-ordinate with a proton.

Some common basic species are

$$\ddot{O}:H \qquad\qquad H:\overset{\displaystyle H}{\underset{\displaystyle H}{\ddot{N}}}: \qquad\qquad \ddot{O}:\overset{\displaystyle :\ddot{O}:}{C}:\ddot{O}:$$

| hydroxyl ion | ammonia | anion of weak acid (carbonate), neglecting bond equalisation |

and they react according to the equations

$$OH^- + H^+ \longrightarrow H_2O \qquad\qquad (1)$$

$$NH_3 + H^+ \longrightarrow NH_4^+ \qquad\qquad (2)$$

$$CO_3^{2-} + 2H^+ \longrightarrow H_2CO_3 \longrightarrow CO_2 + H_2O \qquad (3)$$

Types of base

There are four main types

(*a*) *Soluble metal oxides and hydroxides*—i.e. oxides and hydroxides of Group I metals and the alkaline earth metals of Group II (e.g. NaOH, KOH, Ca(OH)$_2$, Ba(OH)$_2$)

Water soluble hydroxides are known as **alkalis**. They are strong bases in that, being completely dissociated in solution, they yield high concentrations of hydroxyl ions. They react with acids by reaction (1) above. Although, strictly speaking, it is the OH^- species which is the base the term is commonly applied to the compound containing or giving rise to it.

Soluble metal oxides yield alkalis with water

$$O^{2-} + H_2O \longrightarrow 2OH^-$$

(b) *Sparingly soluble metal oxides and hydroxides*

These yield very dilute solutions containing hydroxyl ions, e.g.

$$\underset{\text{solid}}{ZnO} + H_2O \rightleftharpoons \underbrace{Zn^{2+} + 2OH^-}_{\text{solution}} \qquad (4)$$

Reaction with acids proceeds as (1) above, and equilibrium (4) is displaced to the right, i.e. the base dissolves.

Bases of this type are weak because, having low solubility, they yield very low concentrations of OH^- ions in aqueous solution.

(c) *Salts of weak acids*, e.g. Na_2CO_3, $CaCO_3$, CH_3COONa

These react with stronger acids according to (3) above (or similar equations)—the weaker acid being formed by proton transfer.

(d) *Covalent bases*, e.g. NH_3 and its derivatives (CH_3NH_2, etc.)

These can accept protons direct from an acid as in (2) above, or they can react with water

$$NH_3 + H_2O \rightleftharpoons NH_4^+ + OH^- \qquad (5)$$

to yield hydroxyl ions which then react as in (1).

These bases are weak since equilibrium (5) (and similar systems) lies well to the left. Although a weak base, aqueous ammonia is commonly known as an alkali.

OXIDES (AND HYDROXIDES)

There are seven types of oxide.

(1) Basic oxides

These react with acids (and acidic oxides) but not bases, to form salts.

Basic oxides of Group I metals and Ca, Sr, Ba, are water soluble, reacting to give soluble hydroxides (alkalis)

$$CaO + H_2O \longrightarrow Ca(OH)_2 \quad \text{or} \quad O^{2-} + H_2O \longrightarrow 2OH^-$$

Basic oxides and hydroxides of other metals are sparingly soluble in water, e.g.

$$CuO + H_2O \rightleftharpoons Cu^{2+} + 2OH^-$$

Reactions with acids:

$$H^+ + OH^- \longrightarrow H_2O$$

leaving the metal cation and acid radical together in solution as the components of a salt.

Reactions with acidic oxides: see below.

(2) Acidic oxides (also called acid anhydrides)

These react with bases, but not acids or acidic oxides, to form salts. They are usually water soluble, yielding acids.

Acidic oxides are usually non-metal oxides, e.g. SO_2, SO_3, CO_2, P_4O_{10}, Cl_2O_7, SiO_2, but some higher oxides of metals are acidic, e.g. Mn_2O_7,

with alkalis:
$$SO_2 + 2OH^- \longrightarrow H_2O + SO_3^{2-} \text{ (sulphite), excess alkali}$$
$$SO_2 + H_2O + SO_3^{2-} \longrightarrow 2HSO_3^- \text{ (hydrogen sulphite),}$$
$$\text{excess acidic oxide}$$

with basic oxides:
$$SiO_2 + CaO \longrightarrow CaSiO_3$$

with water:
$$CO_2 + H_2O \rightleftharpoons H_2CO_3 \rightleftharpoons H^+ + HCO_3^- \rightleftharpoons$$
$$2H^+ + CO_3^{2-}$$

(3) Neutral oxides

These react neither with acids nor alkalis to form salts. Common examples are NO, N_2O. CO is frequently included here but with conc. aq. NaOH under pressure it yields sodium formate

$$CO + OH^- \longrightarrow HCOO^-$$

and so could be classified as acidic.

(4) Amphoteric oxides

These react both with acids (and acidic oxides) and alkalis to form salts, e.g. ZnO, PbO, SnO, Al_2O_3.

Hydroxides of these metals react similarly. The oxides and hydroxides are sparingly soluble in water.

In water two dissociations occur

$$2H^+ + ZnO_2{}^{2-} \rightleftharpoons ZnO + H_2O \rightleftharpoons Zn^{2+} + 2OH^-$$
$$\text{(or } Zn(OH)_2)$$

Addition of alkali removes H^+ ions and the system moves to the left, yielding a zincate. Addition of acid removes OH^- ions and the system shifts to the right, yielding the zinc salt of the acid concerned.

(5) Peroxides

These yield hydrogen peroxide when treated with cold dilute acid, e.g.

$$BaO_2 + H_2SO_4 \longrightarrow H_2O_2 + BaSO_4$$
$$\text{or} \qquad O_2{}^{2-} + 2H^+ \longrightarrow H_2O_2$$

They are ionic, containing the peroxide ion $[O\!-\!O]^{2-}$, and may be regarded as salts of the very weak acid hydrogen peroxide. They are formed only by highly electropositive metals and are powerful oxidising agents.

(6) Dioxides

Some metals (the commonest are Pb and Mn) yield oxides of

formula MO_2 which do not give hydrogen peroxide with acids but oxidise hydrochloric acid to chlorine, e.g.

$$MnO_2 + 4HCl \longrightarrow MnCl_2 + Cl_2 + 2H_2O$$

They yield oxygen when treated with conc. sulphuric acid

$$2MnO_2 + 2H_2SO_4 \longrightarrow 2MnSO_4 + 2H_2O + O_2$$

and are also amphoteric

$$PbO_2 + 4HCl \text{ (ice cold, conc.)} \longrightarrow PbCl_4 + 2H_2O$$
$$PbO_2 + 2NaOH \text{ (conc., aq.)} \longrightarrow Na_2PbO_3 + H_2O$$

(7) Compound (mixed) oxides

These behave as if they were mixtures of two other oxides of the same metal, i.e. the metal concerned is present in two valency states, e.g. Fe_3O_4 behaves like FeO,Fe_2O_3 and Pb_3O_4 like $2PbO,PbO_2$. Thus with a dilute acid Fe_3O_4 yields a solution containing both Fe^{2+} and Fe^{3+} ions

$$Fe_3O_4 + 8H^+ \longrightarrow Fe^{2+} + 2Fe^{3+} + 4H_2O$$

and red lead yields a lead(II) solution and a brown precipitate of lead(IV) oxide with nitric acid

$$Pb_3O_4 + 4H^+ \longrightarrow 2Pb^{2+} + PbO_2 + 2H_2O$$

SALTS

A salt is formed when the hydrogen ions produced by an acid are replaced by metal ions (or ammonium etc.). The vast majority are predominantly electrovalent in character.

A few compounds usually called salts are predominantly covalent, e.g. $HgCl_2$, and anhydrous iron(III) chloride. These usually sublime readily and some are weak electrolytes.

Normal and acid salts

A normal salt is said to be formed when the 'acid hydrogen' replacement is complete, e.g. K_2CO_3, NH_4Cl, $CuSO_4$.

An acid salt is produced when the 'acid hydrogen' replacement is incomplete, e.g. $KHCO_3$, $NaHSO_4$, Na_2HPO_4.

Acid salts are normally formed from acids with a basicity > 1. An exception is KHF_2 and this is only formed because of the high degree of hydrogen bonding in the ion $[F\text{----}H\text{----}F]^-$ (see p. 35).

It should be noted that acid salts seldom give an acid solution (i.e. pH < 7) since their anions are usually those of weak acids— capturing H^+ ions to leave an excess of OH^- ions in aqueous solution, e.g. for Na_2HPO_4

$$HPO_4^{2-} + H^+ \rightleftharpoons H_2PO_4^-$$

Hydrogen sulphates are, however, acidic since sulphuric acid is strong and the hydrogen sulphate ion dissociates appreciably

$$HSO_4^- \rightleftharpoons H^+ + SO_4^{2-}$$

Basic salts

Some examples of basic salts are $2PbCO_3,Pb(OH)_2$ (white lead), $Mg(OH)Cl$, $Zn(OH)Cl$, $BiOCl$. Little is known about their structure and many may in fact be mixtures of the normal salt and the parent base.

Basic salts are sparingly soluble in water, and many are produced by hydrolysis of normal salts, e.g.

$$SnCl_2 + H_2O \rightleftharpoons Sn(OH)Cl + HCl \tag{1}$$

$$BiCl_3 + H_2O \rightleftharpoons BiOCl + 2HCl \tag{2}$$

Most insoluble carbonates are basic and are prepared by double decomposition precipitation reactions. This is because both carbonate and hydroxyl ions are present in aqueous sodium carbonate due to the hydrolysis

$$CO_3^{2-} + H_2O \rightleftharpoons HCO_3^- + OH^-$$

and so with, say, a copper(II) salt solution

$$Cu^{2+} + CO_3^{2-} \longrightarrow CuCO_3 \ \big\rbrace \text{ basic salt; probably}$$
$$Cu^{2+} + 2OH^- \longrightarrow Cu(OH)_2 \big/ \text{ a mixture}$$

Basic salts are soluble in dilute acids, e.g. reactions (1) and (2) above are reversible.

Double salts

Double salts are said to be formed when two salts in the same solution crystallise as one—the crystals formed containing the ionic species of both, e.g.

ammonium iron(II) sulphate	$(NH_4)_2SO_4,FeSO_4,6H_2O$
potassium chromium(III) sulphate	
(chrome alum)	$K_2SO_4,Cr_2(SO_4)_3,24H_2O$
potassium magnesium chloride	
(carnallite)	$KCl,MgCl_2,6H_2O$

The chemical properties exhibited by a double salt are those of the component salts but the physical characteristics (e.g. crystalline shape) may differ considerably from those of the component salts.

Complex salts

A complex ion is an ion produced when one ionic species combines with another (or with a molecule), e.g.

$$Fe^{2+} + 6CN^- \rightleftharpoons Fe(CN)_6^{4-}$$
$$Cu^{2+} + 4NH_3 \rightleftharpoons Cu(NH_3)_4^{2+}$$

and a complex salt is one which contains a complex ion.

Complex salts undergo two dissociations in aqueous solution. The first is virtually complete

$$K_4Fe(CN)_6 \rightleftharpoons 4K^+ + Fe(CN)_6^{4-}$$

The second, involving the dissociation of the complex ion itself, occurs to a much lesser extent

$$Fe(CN)_6^{4-} \rightleftharpoons Fe^{2+} + 6CN^- \tag{1}$$

In the case of potassium hexacyanoferrate(II), the solution gives reactions of K^+ ions and $Fe(CN)_6^{4-}$ but not of Fe^{2+} and CN^-

ions—this is because the hexacyanoferrate(II) ion is very stable and equilibrium (1) lies almost entirely to the left.

Some complex salts give solutions in which the dissociation of the complex ion is appreciable, e.g. potassium tetracyano-cadmiate(II) dissociates

$$K_2Cd(CN)_4 \rightleftharpoons 2K^+ + Cd(CN)_4^{2-}$$
$$Cd(CN)_4^{2-} \rightleftharpoons Cd^{2+} + 4CN^-$$

and yields a sufficiently high concentration of Cd^{2+} ions to give a yellow precipitate of CdS with soluble sulphides.

Ions and molecules involved in complex ion formation possess lone pairs, e.g.

$$[:C \equiv N:]^- \qquad :NH_3 \qquad \left[:\overset{..}{\underset{..}{I}}:\right]^-$$

(N.B. carbon lone pair used)

and the complexing is effected by dative bond formation, e.g.

$$\left[\begin{array}{c} NH_3 \\ \downarrow \\ H_3N{\rightarrow}Cu{\leftarrow}NH_3 \\ \uparrow \\ NH_3 \end{array} \right]^{2+}$$

The number of lone pairs co-ordinated onto a metal ion (or the number of monodentate *ligands*) is called the co-ordination *number* (C.N.) of the ion—i.e. 4 for Cu^{2+}, 6 for Fe^{2+}.

The co-ordination number of an ion is characteristic of the ion. Most ions have C.N. = 4, e.g. Hg^{2+}, Hg_2^{2+}, Ni^{2+}, Cu^{2+}; but for Fe^{2+}, Fe^{3+}, C.N. = 6 and for Ag^+ C.N. = 2.

OXIDISING AND REDUCING AGENTS AND REDOX REACTIONS

The original concept of oxidation as being the addition of oxygen or the removal of hydrogen, and of reduction as the removal of oxygen or the addition of hydrogen, is too narrow to be of general value. The wider concept of oxidation number (O.N.) covers all oxidation–reduction (redox) reactions.

Oxidation number

The O.N. of an element may be computed using the following rules:

(a) The sum of the O.Ns. of the elements in any compound = 0.

(b) The O.N. of an uncombined element = 0.

(c) The O.N. of an ion = its charge.

(d) The O.N. of combined hydrogen = +1, except in ionic metal hydrides when it is −1.

(e) The O.N. of combined oxygen = −2, except in peroxides when it is −1 (and in fluorine oxides it becomes positive).

Some examples of O.N. calculation:

N in HNO_3:
$$\left. \begin{array}{l} H = +1, \\ 3O = -2 \times 3 = -6 \end{array} \right\} \quad \therefore N = +5$$

S in Na_2SO_3:
$$\left. \begin{array}{l} 2Na^+ = +2, \\ 3O = -2 \times 3 = -6 \end{array} \right\} \quad \therefore S = +4$$

P in H_3PO_4:
$$\left. \begin{array}{l} 3H = +1 \times 3 = +3, \\ 4O = -2 \times 4 = -8 \end{array} \right\} \quad \therefore P = +5$$

Mn in $KMnO_4$:
$$\left. \begin{array}{l} K^+ = +1, \\ 4O = -2 \times 4 = -8 \end{array} \right\} \quad \therefore Mn = +7$$

S in $BaSO_4$:
$$\left. \begin{array}{l} Ba^{2+} = +2, \\ 4O = -2 \times 4 = -8 \end{array} \right\} \quad \therefore S = +6$$

Cr in $K_2Cr_2O_7$:
$$\left. \begin{array}{l} 2K^+ = +2, \\ 7O = -2 \times 7 = -14 \end{array} \right\} \quad \begin{array}{l} \therefore 2Cr = +12, \\ \therefore \; Cr = +6 \end{array}$$

Oxidation is a process in which an O.N. is increased.
Reduction is a process in which an O.N. is decreased.

Some examples of oxidation and reduction:

$FeCl_2 \longrightarrow FeCl_3$ is oxidation,
as O.N. of Fe increases $+2 \rightarrow +3$

$HNO_3 \longrightarrow NH_3$ is reduction,
as O.N. of N decreases $+5 \rightarrow -3$

$H_2O_2 \longrightarrow H_2O$ is reduction,
as O.N. of O decreases $-1 \rightarrow -2$

$KMnO_4 \longrightarrow Mn^{2+}$ is reduction,
as O.N. of Mn decreases $+7 \rightarrow +2$

$HCl \longrightarrow Cl_2$ is oxidation,
as O.N. of Cl increases $-1 \rightarrow 0$

$P_4 \longrightarrow PCl_5$ is oxidation,
as O.N. of P increases $0 \rightarrow +5$

Ionic redox reactions

The section above has dealt with redox in general. It is convenient to consider some important ionic redox reactions as a separate topic.

Oxidation is a process in which electrons are lost by atoms or ions, e.g. iron(II) to iron(III)

$$Fe^{2+} \longrightarrow Fe^{3+} + e \qquad (1)$$

Reduction is a process in which electrons are gained by atoms or ions, e.g. chlorine to chloride ions

$$Cl_2 + 2e \longrightarrow 2Cl^- \qquad (2)$$

In an ionic redox reaction electrons are transferred from the reducing agent to the oxidising agent; in the oxidation of Fe^{2+} ions by chlorine, electrons are transferred from the Fe^{2+} ions to the Cl_2. The redox equation is given by $2 \times (1) +$ (2), eliminating electrons

$$2Fe^{2+} + Cl_2 \longrightarrow 2Fe^{3+} + 2Cl^-$$

Substance	Partial ionic equation
Oxidants	
Acid permanganate	$MnO_4^- + 8H^+ + 5e \rightarrow Mn^{2+} + 4H_2O$
Chlorine	$Cl_2 + 2e \rightarrow 2Cl^-$
Acid dichromate	$Cr_2O_7^{2-} + 14H^+ + 6e \rightarrow 2Cr^{3+} + 7H_2O$
Bromine	$Br_2 + 2e \rightarrow 2Br^-$
Dil. nitric acid	$NO_3^- + 4H^+ + 3e \rightarrow NO + 2H_2O$
Iron(III) salts	$Fe^{3+} + e \rightarrow Fe^{2+}$
Iodine	$I_2 + 2e \rightarrow 2I^-$
Acid hydrogen peroxide	$H_2O_2 + 2H^+ + 2e \rightarrow 2H_2O$
Reductants	
Hydrogen	$H_2 \rightarrow 2H^+ + 2e$
Metals*	$M \rightarrow M^{n+} + ne$
Hydrogen sulphide	$H_2S \rightarrow 2H^+ + S + 2e$
Iron(II) salts	$Fe^{2+} \rightarrow Fe^{3+} + e$
Oxalates	$C_2O_4^{2-} \rightarrow 2CO_2 + 2e$
Thiosulphates	$2S_2O_3^{2-} \rightarrow S_4O_6^{2-} + 2e$

* The E.C.S. (see Chapter 2) gives the order of strength of the metals as reducing agents—the higher the metal, the greater its reducing power.

Thus one may define:

An *oxidising agent* (oxidant) as a substance which gains electrons and is itself reduced.

A *reducing agent* (reductant) as a substance which loses electrons and is itself oxidised.

Some common oxidants and reductants are included in the table opposite.

Displacement reactions

This description is applied to those redox reactions in which an element is displaced from one of its compounds by another element, e.g.

$$Zn + Cu^{2+} \longrightarrow Zn^{2+} + Cu \quad \text{(Zn oxidised, } Cu^{2+} \text{ reduced)}$$
$$Cl_2 + 2Br^- \longrightarrow 2Cl^- + Br_2 \quad \text{(Cl}_2 \text{ reduced, } Br^- \text{ oxidised)}$$

Disproportionation reactions

Disproportionation is said to occur when a reaction results in both the oxidation and reduction of one of the reactants, e.g.

Cu^+ ions are unstable in aqueous solution and yield Cu^{2+} ions and the metal

$$2Cu^+ \longrightarrow Cu^{2+} + Cu$$

Manganates (Mn VI) are rapidly hydrolysed by water or dilute acid to permanganates (Mn VII) and manganese(IV) oxide

$$3MnO_4^{2-} + 2H_2O \longrightarrow 2MnO_4^- + MnO_2 + 4OH^-$$

ACID CHLORIDES (also bromides; iodides less stable)

These compounds may be regarded as being formed by replacing the hydroxyl groups of acids by chlorine atoms, e.g.

sulphuric acid, H_2SO_4 or $SO_2(OH)_2$;
sulphuryl chloride, SO_2Cl_2

sulphurous acid, H_2SO_3 or $SO(OH)_2$;
thionyl chloride, $SOCl_2$

chromic acid, H_2CrO_4 or $CrO_2(OH)_2$;
chromyl chloride, CrO_2Cl_2

orthophosphoric acid H_3PO_4 or $PO(OH)_3$;
phosphorus oxychloride, $POCl_3$

They are covalent fuming liquids which are readily hydrolysed to give the parent acids and hydrogen chloride, e.g.

$$SO_2Cl_2 + 2H_2O \longrightarrow H_2SO_4 + 2HCl$$

COVALENT CHLORIDES (also bromides and some iodides)
These are liquids or easily sublimed solids. They are formed by the majority of non-metals and by some metals. Many fume in moist air due to rapid hydrolysis.

Some examples:

PCl_3, CCl_4, $SiCl_4$, $SnCl_4$	colourless liquids
S_2Cl_2, $PbCl_4$ (very unstable)	pale yellow liquids
Al_2Cl_6, $HgCl_2$, PCl_5	white solids
Fe_2Cl_6	black (often purplish-brown) solid
$CrCl_3$	purple solid

The majority may be prepared by passing chlorine over the heated element. Most are readily hydrolysed, yielding hydrogen chloride; other products vary considerably but many yield hydroxy compounds, i.e. metal hydroxides or oxyacids; reference should be made to the flowsheets.

DISSOCIATION AND DECOMPOSITION

Dissociation

This is the reversible splitting up of molecules (or ions) to yield simpler molecules (or ions), e.g.

$$PCl_5 \rightleftharpoons PCl_3 + Cl_2$$
$$NH_4Cl \rightleftharpoons NH_3 + HCl$$

(A mathematical treatment of dissociation is given in the Chemical Equilibrium chapters of *Revision Notes for Advanced Level Physical Chemistry*.)

Decomposition

This is the irreversible splitting up of molecules (or ions) to yield simpler species, e.g.

$$2Pb(NO_3)_2 \longrightarrow 2PbO + 4NO_2 + O_2$$
$$2H_2O_2 \longrightarrow 2H_2O + O_2$$

DOUBLE DECOMPOSITION

This term is usually applied to precipitation reactions in which the component ions of the precipitated compound originate from two other compounds (usually in aqueous soln.), e.g.

$$2NaOH + CuSO_4 \longrightarrow Cu(OH)_2 \downarrow + Na_2SO_4$$

or $\qquad 2OH^- + Cu^{2+} \longrightarrow Cu(OH)_2 \downarrow$

the 'unused' ions giving a fourth compound in solution. Occasionally reactions of this type involve all ions in precipitation, e.g.

$$Ag_2SO_4 + BaCl_2 \longrightarrow BaSO_4 \downarrow + 2AgCl \downarrow$$

HYDROLYSIS, HYDRATION AND DEHYDRATION

Hydrolysis is said to occur when a substance reacts with water in such a way that two compounds are produced—one containing H atoms from the water and the other the corresponding OH groups, i.e.

$$X\text{-}Y + H\text{-}OH \longrightarrow H\text{-}Y + X\text{-}OH$$

Some important types of inorganic substances which may be hydrolysed are

(*a*) acid chlorides, e.g.

$$SO_2Cl_2 + 2H_2O \longrightarrow 2HCl + SO_2(OH)_2 \ (i.e. \ H_2SO_4)$$

(b) covalent chlorides, e.g.

$$PCl_3 + 3H_2O \longrightarrow 3HCl + P(OH)_3 \text{ (i.e. } H_3PO_3)$$

(c) halogens, e.g.

$$Cl_2 + H_2O \rightleftharpoons HCl + HOCl$$

(d) compounds of metals and non-metals, e.g.

$$Mg_3N_2 + 6H_2O \longrightarrow 2NH_3 + 3Mg(OH)_2$$

(e) salts

All salts (except those of a strong acid and a strong base, e.g. NaCl) are hydrolysed in aqueous solution, and their solutions are not neutral (i.e. pH ≠ 7), e.g.

iron(III) salts†

$$Fe^{3+} + 3H_2O \rightleftharpoons Fe(OH)_3 + 3H^+ \quad (pH < 7)$$

carbonates

$$CO_3^{2-} + 2H_2O \rightleftharpoons H_2CO_3 + 2OH^- \quad (pH > 7)$$

Hydration is a process in which water (or the elements of water, i.e. 2H and O) is added to a substance.
Three important types of hydration are

(a) anhydrous salts giving hydrates, e.g.

$$CuSO_4 + 5H_2O \longrightarrow CuSO_4,5H_2O$$

(b) acid oxides (acid anhydrides) giving acids, e.g.

$$SO_2 + H_2O \longrightarrow H_2SO_3$$

(c) basic oxides of metals of Groups I and II giving hydroxides, e.g.

$$CaO + H_2O \longrightarrow Ca(OH)_2$$

---

† This type of reaction is dealt with more fully under aluminium (p. 48), and a detailed consideration of salt hydrolysis is given in *Revision Notes for Advanced Level Physical Chemistry* (pp. 67–69).

Ions in aqueous solution are usually hydrated, even if they are not already in this state in the crystal lattice. Water molecules are polarised

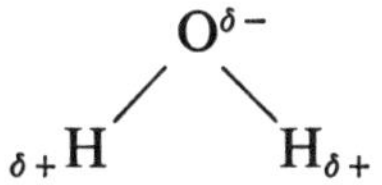

$$O^{\delta-}$$
$${}_{\delta+}H \qquad H_{\delta+}$$

and ions of Groups I and II metals are hydrated by ion-dipole attraction, e.g.

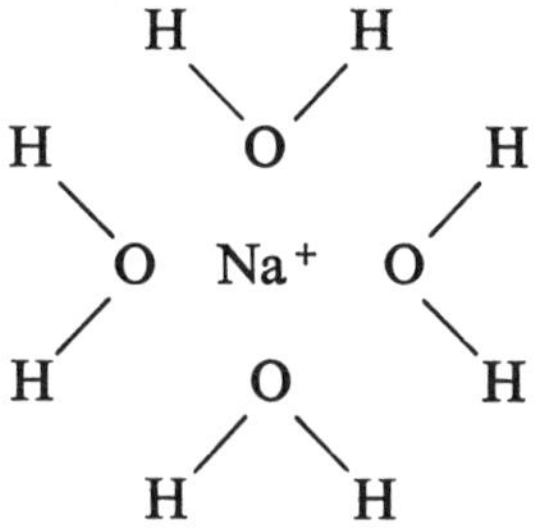

$$
\begin{array}{ccc}
H & & H \\
& O & \\
H & & H \\
O & Na^+ & O \\
H & & H \\
& O & \\
H & & H
\end{array}
$$

Most other metal ions are hydrated by dative bond formation, e.g.

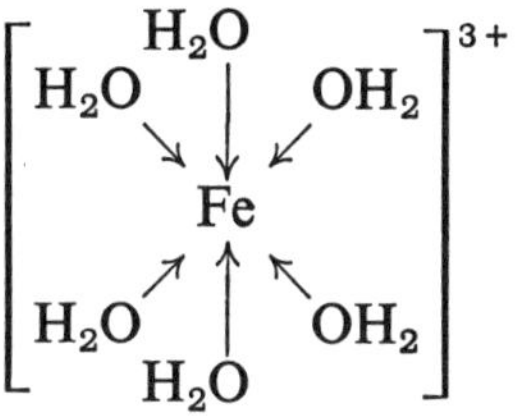

$$\left[\begin{array}{ccc} & H_2O & \\ H_2O & & OH_2 \\ & Fe & \\ H_2O & & OH_2 \\ & H_2O & \end{array} \right]^{3+}$$

Simple anions are hydrated by ion-dipole attraction (orientation of water molecules reversed, i.e. H's nearer X^-). With oxy-anions hydrogen bonding is often significant.

   Dehydration is the reverse of hydration. Concentrated sulphuric acid is the commonest dehydrating agent and phosphorus pentoxide the most powerful. Dehydration is often effected by heating.

Inorganic compounds which may often be dehydrated are salt hydrates, acid salts, metal hydroxides and acids, e.g.

$$FeSO_4,7H_2O \longrightarrow FeSO_4 + 7H_2O$$
$$2NaHSO_4 \longrightarrow Na_2S_2O_7 + H_2O$$
$$2Al(OH)_3 \longrightarrow Al_2O_3 + 3H_2O$$
$$H_2SO_3 \longrightarrow SO_2 + H_2O$$

HYDRIDES

There are two main types (i) salt-like (ionic), (ii) volatile (molecular).

Salt-like hydrides

These are electrovalent and contain the ionic species H^-. They are formed by the alkali metals and the alkaline earths. When hydrogen is passed over the heated metal (ideal temperatures varying between 150°–700° C) and are colourless (or white) when pure

$$2Na + H_2 \longrightarrow 2(Na^+ H^-)$$
$$Ca + H_2 \longrightarrow Ca^{2+} H^- H^-$$

They are used as sources of hydrogen (particularly CaH_2) in situations which rule out heavy cylinders. All ionic hydrides yield hydrogen with water

$$H^- + H_2O \longrightarrow H_2 + OH^-$$

Some (especially LiH, which is very stable) are used as powerful reducing agents.

Volatile hydrides

These are formed by the non-metals and by the weakly electropositive metals of Groups III, IV and V. The majority of the simple species (e.g. CH_4, NH_3, H_2S, HI) are either gases or highly volatile liquids at room temperature.

Thermal stability decreases as groups are descended, e.g.

$$CH_4 > SiH_4 > GeH_4 > SnH_4 > PbH_4$$

The particularly stable C—C bond enables carbon to form many long and branched-chain hydrides of the type

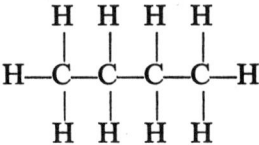

Boron and silicon also possess this property, but to a much lesser extent.

The hydrides H_2O and HF have unexpectedly high boiling points, due to extensive hydrogen bonding (see p. 35 of this book and also p. 17 of *Revision Notes for Advanced Level Physical Chemistry*).

Chapter 4

Group Comparisons and Element Flowsheets

SECTION A: HYDROGEN

	Atomic number	Electronic configuration of atom
H	1	1

The hydrogen atom is the simplest of atoms—the nucleus is a proton, and thus it has only one orbital electron. There are two other isotopes of the element, both of which are rare (i) deuterium $_1^2H$ (or D), 0.015%, nucleus: 1 proton + 1 neutron; (ii) tritium $_1^3H$ (or T), $10^{-19}\%$, nucleus: 1 proton + 2 neutrons.

The hydrogen atom has one electron fewer than that of the following noble gas helium. Thus it is invariably univalent and can attain the stable helium configuration in two ways.

(i) **By gaining an electron to form the uninegative ion H^-**

This is encountered in the hydrides of the highly electropositive metals of Groups I and II, i.e. $Li \to Cs$ and $Ca \to Ba$. Here the hydrogen atom acquires an electron from the metal and an ionic, crystalline hydride is formed, containing the H^- ion, e.g.

$$\begin{array}{ccccccc} Na & + & H & \to & Na^+ & & H^- \\ 2, 8, 1 & & 1 & & 2, 8 & & 2 \end{array}$$

Hydrides of this type are rapidly attacked by water, liberating hydrogen

$$H^- + H_2O \longrightarrow OH^- + H_2$$

(ii) **By sharing a pair of electrons** to form

(a) *a single covalent bond* as in HCl, CH_4, NH_3. Covalent hydrides are usually either gases or volatile liquids; they are formed mainly with non-metals and with these elements are quite stable. Similar compounds are formed with several of the less electropositive metals (e.g. SnH_4) but these are unstable. The chemical nature of a hydride depends on the character of the other element (see table on p. 8).

(b) *a dative (or co-ordinate) bond* as in H_3O^+, NH_4^+. The simple H^+ ion is a proton, i.e. the atom less its electron. This rarely exists as a separate particle under normal conditions. In solutions it is usually attached to a solvent molecule (i.e. it is solvated) by dative bond formation. Thus in water the 'hydrogen' ion is H_3O^+

$$\left[\begin{array}{c} H\!-\!O\!\rightarrow\!H \\ | \\ H \end{array} \right]^+$$

This particle is the hydroxonium ion.

THE HYDROGEN BOND

Hydrogen can act as a 'link' between atoms of highly electronegative elements such as F, O, and N by formation of the so-called hydrogen bond.

The bond is essentially electrostatic in nature and results from the considerable polarisation of the covalent bond between hydrogen and an atom of one of these elements, e.g.

$$\overset{\delta +}{H}\!\overset{\delta -}{\underset{\bullet}{\cdot}F}$$
polarised bond

hydrogen bonding

This association accounts for the abnormally high b.ps. of HF, H_2O, NH_3 and the existence of the HF_2^- ion which is $[F\!-\!H\cdots F]^-$.

POSITION OF HYDROGEN IN THE PERIODIC TABLE

The first period of the classification contains only two elements, hydrogen and helium, and while the position of helium presents no difficulty (being clearly the first member of Group O—the noble gases), hydrogen has no obvious position.

It could be placed at the head of Group I by virtue of its forming a hydrated unipositive ion—like the alkali metals. With possibly more reason it could be placed in Group VII since it forms a uninegative ion in the 'salt-like' hydrides and exhibits unicovalence in its compounds with non-metals.

Apart from the above examples, hydrogen bears little resemblance to the elements of these groups and it is probably best considered apart.

CHEMICAL PROPERTIES

(a) **Important reactions with other elements**

(i) *non-metals* which react with hydrogen give covalent hydrides, e.g.

$$2H_2 + O_2 \longrightarrow 2H_2O$$ hydrogen burns in oxygen (explosively if the proportions are 2:1 by volume) liberating much energy—H_2 is an important constituent of the fuel gases coal gas and water gas.

$$H_2 + Cl_2 \longrightarrow 2HCl$$ hydrogen burns in chlorine (also explosively if proportions are 1:1 by volume)—commercial source of HCl.

$$3H_2 + N_2 \rightleftharpoons 2NH_3$$ combination occurs under high pressure in the presence of an iron catalyst (see Haber Process, p. 127).

(ii) *metals* such as Na, Ca, i.e. members of Groups I and II, yield ionic hydrides (see above).

(b) **Many metal oxides are reduced to the metal** when heated in a stream of the gas (see also E.C.S., p. 11).

$$CuO + H_2 \longrightarrow Cu + H_2O$$
$$Fe_3O_4 + 4H_2 \rightleftharpoons 3Fe + 4H_2O$$

(equilibrium displaced completely to the right if steam is swept away in the hydrogen stream).

(c) **Hydrogenation.** Three major uses of hydrogen are given on the previous page. Other important uses lie (formally) in the field of organic chemistry. Methanol is manufactured by a catalysed combination reaction between carbon monoxide and hydrogen.

Hydrogenation of soft oils is important in the manufacture of vegetable-based margarines and cooking fats. Hydrogen is passed into, for example, groundnut oil in which is suspended a finely divided nickel catalyst. The $\diagup C{=}C\diagdown$ bonds of the oil are saturated, and the modified oil produced has an appreciably higher melting point, more suitable for the manufacture of margarine.

$$
\begin{array}{l}
CH_3(CH_2)_7CH{=}CH(CH_2)_7COOCH_2 \\
\qquad\qquad\qquad\qquad\qquad\quad | \\
CH_3(CH_2)_7CH{=}CH(CH_2)_7COOCH \quad + 3H_2 \longrightarrow \\
\qquad\qquad\qquad\qquad\qquad\quad | \\
CH_3(CH_2)_7CH{=}CH(CH_2)_7COOCH_2
\end{array}
$$

$$
\begin{array}{l}
CH_3(CH_2)_{16}COOCH_2 \\
\qquad\qquad\qquad\quad | \\
CH_3(CH_2)_{16}COOCH \\
\qquad\qquad\qquad\quad | \\
CH_3(CH_2)_{16}COOCH_2
\end{array}
$$

SECTION B
GROUP I: THE ALKALI METALS

	Atomic number	Electronic configuration of atoms
Li	3	2, 1
Na	11	2, 8, 1
K	19	2, 8, 8, 1
Rb	37	2, 8, 18, 8, 1
Cs	55	2, 8, 18, 18, 8, 1

Atoms of these elements contain one electron more than those of the noble gases. Thus they are univalent, readily losing the outer electron to form a positive ion

$$M \longrightarrow M^+ + e$$

A large atomic radius facilitates the loss of outer electrons since the attraction by the nucleus is weaker. Alkali metals have comparatively large atomic radii (see p. 5) and, in addition, need to lose only one electron to attain a stable, noble gas configuration; this makes them the most reactive metals in their periods. Reactivity increases with atomic radius, Li $\rightarrow$ Cs. Lithium is in many ways similar to magnesium (diagonal relationship, p. 7).

CHEMICAL PROPERTIES

Elements

(*a*) The metals burn vigorously when heated in air or oxygen to form first the basic oxide M_2O

$$4Na + O_2 \longrightarrow 2Na_2O$$

and then higher oxides if the oxygen is in excess, e.g. Na_2O_2 (sodium peroxide), KO_2 (potassium superoxide).

(*b*) All tarnish rapidly when exposed to air (kept under oil).

(*c*) All react vigorously with water to give hydrogen and a solution of the hydroxide

$$2Na + 2H_2O \longrightarrow 2NaOH + H_2$$

(d) All form white crystalline ionic hydrides when heated in hydrogen

$$2Na + H_2 \longrightarrow 2NaH \qquad (Na^+ H^-)$$

Oxides and hydroxides

M_2O—basic oxides; react vigorously with water to give hydroxide solutions

$$M_2O + H_2O \longrightarrow 2MOH$$
i.e. $\qquad O^{2-} + H_2O \longrightarrow 2OH^-$

M_2O_2—peroxides (i.e. $2M^+[O—O]^{2-}$); are thermally stable and may be regarded as salts of the very weak acid hydrogen peroxide; they react with water and dilute acids,

(a) with ice-cold reagent to give hydrogen peroxide solution

$$O_2^{2-} + 2H^+ \longrightarrow H_2O_2$$

(b) at room temperature to give water and oxygen, i.e. the hydrogen peroxide decomposes

$$O_2^{2-} + 2H^+ \longrightarrow H_2O_2 \quad \text{then} \quad 2H_2O_2 \longrightarrow 2H_2O + O_2$$

Peroxides react with carbon dioxide

$$2O_2^{2-} + CO_2 \longrightarrow 2CO_3^{2-} + O_2$$

The hydroxides are highly soluble in water (alkalis). They are strongly basic since their solutions contain high concentrations of hydroxyl ions.

(a) Readily liberate weak bases from their salts

$$NH_4^+ + OH^- \longrightarrow NH_3 \uparrow + H_2O$$

(b) React readily with acids and acidic oxides to give salts

$$NaOH + HNO_3 \longrightarrow NaNO_3 + H_2O$$
$$(\text{i.e. } H^+ + OH^- \longrightarrow H_2O)$$

If the acid is polybasic then excess acid gives acid salts, e.g. with carbon dioxide

$$2OH^- + CO_2 \longrightarrow CO_3^{2-} + H_2O \quad \text{(alkali in excess)}$$
$$CO_3^{2-} + H_2O + CO_2 \longrightarrow 2HCO_3^- \quad \text{(acidic oxide in excess)}$$

(c) Attack Al, Zn, Sn, Pb (slowly) to give hydrogen and solutions containing aluminate, zincate, stannate(II) and plumbate(II) ions.

$$Zn + 2OH^- \longrightarrow ZnO_2^{2-} + H_2$$

(d) React with amphoteric oxides and hydroxides to give salts

$$Al_2O_3 + 2OH^- \longrightarrow H_2O + 2AlO_2^- \quad \text{(aluminate)}$$
$$Sn(OH)_2 + 2OH^- \longrightarrow 2H_2O + SnO_2^{2-} \quad \text{(stannate(II))}$$

(e) React with all non-metals, except C, N, O and the noble gases, under varying conditions to form (among other products) a salt or salts in which the non-metal is contained in the anion

$$Cl_2 + 2OH^- \longrightarrow Cl^- + OCl^- + H_2O$$
$$Si + 2OH^- + H_2O \longrightarrow SiO_3^{2-} + 2H_2$$
$$P_4 + 3OH^- + 3H_2O \longrightarrow 3H_2PO_2^- + PH_3$$

(f) Precipitate insoluble metal hydroxides from metal salt solutions

$$Cu^{2+} + 2OH^- \longrightarrow Cu(OH)_2 \downarrow$$

but if the hydroxide is amphoteric the precipitate dissolves in excess alkali

$$Zn(OH)_2 + 2OH^- \longrightarrow ZnO_2^{2-} + 2H_2O$$

Salts

All contain the colourless ion M^+. Salts of the metals $Na \rightarrow Cs$ are noted for

(i) their almost universal solubility in water and

(ii) their (in most cases) high thermal stability. The sulphates and carbonates do not decompose on heating. Those salts which do decompose usually require strong heating.

(a) Nitrates, on strong heating, melt and then slowly yield nitrites and oxygen

$$2NaNO_3 \longrightarrow 2NaNO_2 + O_2$$

(Continued on page 42)

SODIUM

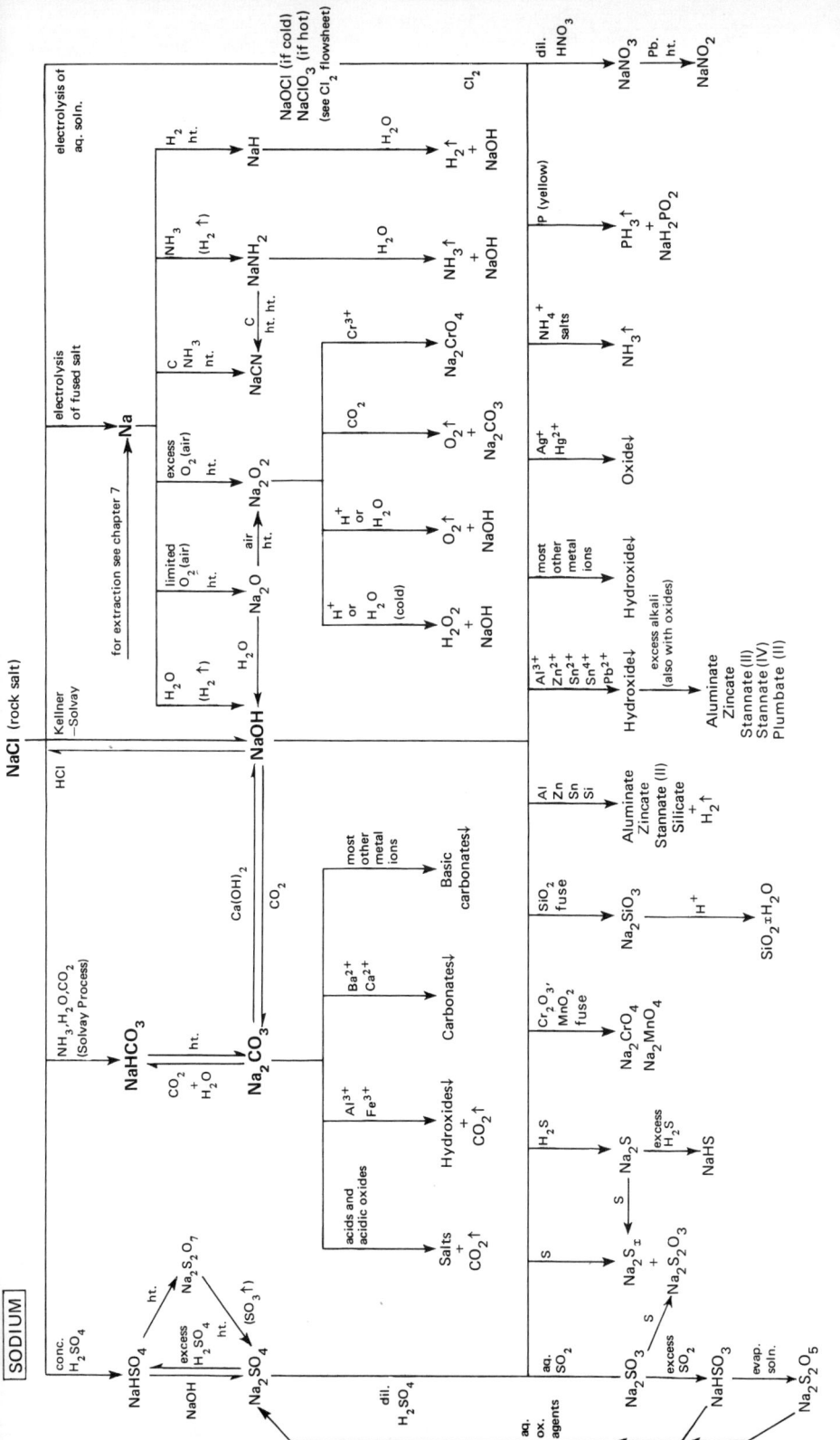

This reduction is more easily effected by heating with a mild reducing agent such as lead

$$NaNO_3 + Pb \longrightarrow NaNO_2 + PbO$$

(b) Only the alkali metals can form hydrogen carbonates which are stable in the solid state, but these decompose very readily on heating (even boiling the solution) to give the normal carbonate

$$2NaHCO_3 \longrightarrow Na_2CO_3 + CO_2 + H_2O$$

i.e. $$2HCO_3{}^- \longrightarrow CO_3{}^{2-} + CO_2 + H_2O$$

(c) Hydrogen sulphates decompose on moderate heating to yield normal sulphates and choking fumes consisting of droplets of concentrated sulphuric acid ($SO_3 + H_2O$)

$$2NaHSO_4 \longrightarrow Na_2SO_4 + SO_3 + H_2O$$

i.e. $$2HSO_4{}^- \longrightarrow SO_4{}^{2-} + SO_3 + H_2O$$

(d) All alkali metal compounds give flame colorations: e.g. Li—red; Na—yellow; K—lilac.

SECTION C
GROUP II: MAGNESIUM and the ALKALINE EARTHS
(Ca, Sr, Ba)

	Atomic number	Electronic configuration of atoms
Mg	12	2, 8, 2
Ca	20	2, 8, 8, 2
Sr	38	2, 8, 18, 8, 2
Ba	56	2, 8, 18, 18, 8, 2

Atoms of these elements contain two electrons more than those of the noble gases and lose their two outer electrons to form ions

$$M \longrightarrow M^{2+} + 2e$$

thus they are divalent but less reactive than the alkali metals (Section B), atoms of which lose only one electron. Like the alkali metals, these Group II metals become more reactive $Mg \rightarrow Ba$, as atomic radius increases.

CHEMICAL PROPERTIES

Elements

(a) All burn when strongly heated in air or oxygen

$$2Mg + O_2 \longrightarrow 2MgO$$

A little nitride is also formed in air.

(b) All tarnish in air (Ba kept under oil).

(c) Ca, Sr, Ba react rapidly with cold water, the solution becoming milky since the hydroxides are not very soluble

$$Ca + 2H_2O \longrightarrow Ca(OH)_2 + H_2$$

(d) All except Mg give ionic hydrides, and all give ionic nitrides, when heated in streams of hydrogen and nitrogen

$$Ba + H_2 \longrightarrow BaH_2 \qquad (Ba^{2+}\ 2H^-)$$
$$3Mg + N_2 \longrightarrow Mg_3N_2 \qquad (3Mg^{2+}\ 2N^{3-})$$

Oxides and Hydroxides

All basic. The oxides of Ca, Sr, Ba react very vigorously with water to give hydroxides, much heat being evolved; MgO reacts slowly.

$$CaO + H_2O \longrightarrow Ca(OH)_2$$

Peroxides are also formed by the alkaline earth metals but these yield oxygen on heating (cf. Na_2O_2, p. 39).

The hydroxides of Ca, Sr and Ba are moderately soluble in water (solubility increasing $Ca \rightarrow Br$) and are classified as alkalis.

Salts

All contain the colourless M^{2+} ion. They are thermally quite stable, though much less so than those of the alkali metals. Mg salts are much more easily decomposed than those of the other members of the group.

(a) The alkaline earth sulphates (e.g. gypsum $CaSO_4,2H_2O$)

(Continued on page 46)

MAGNESIUM

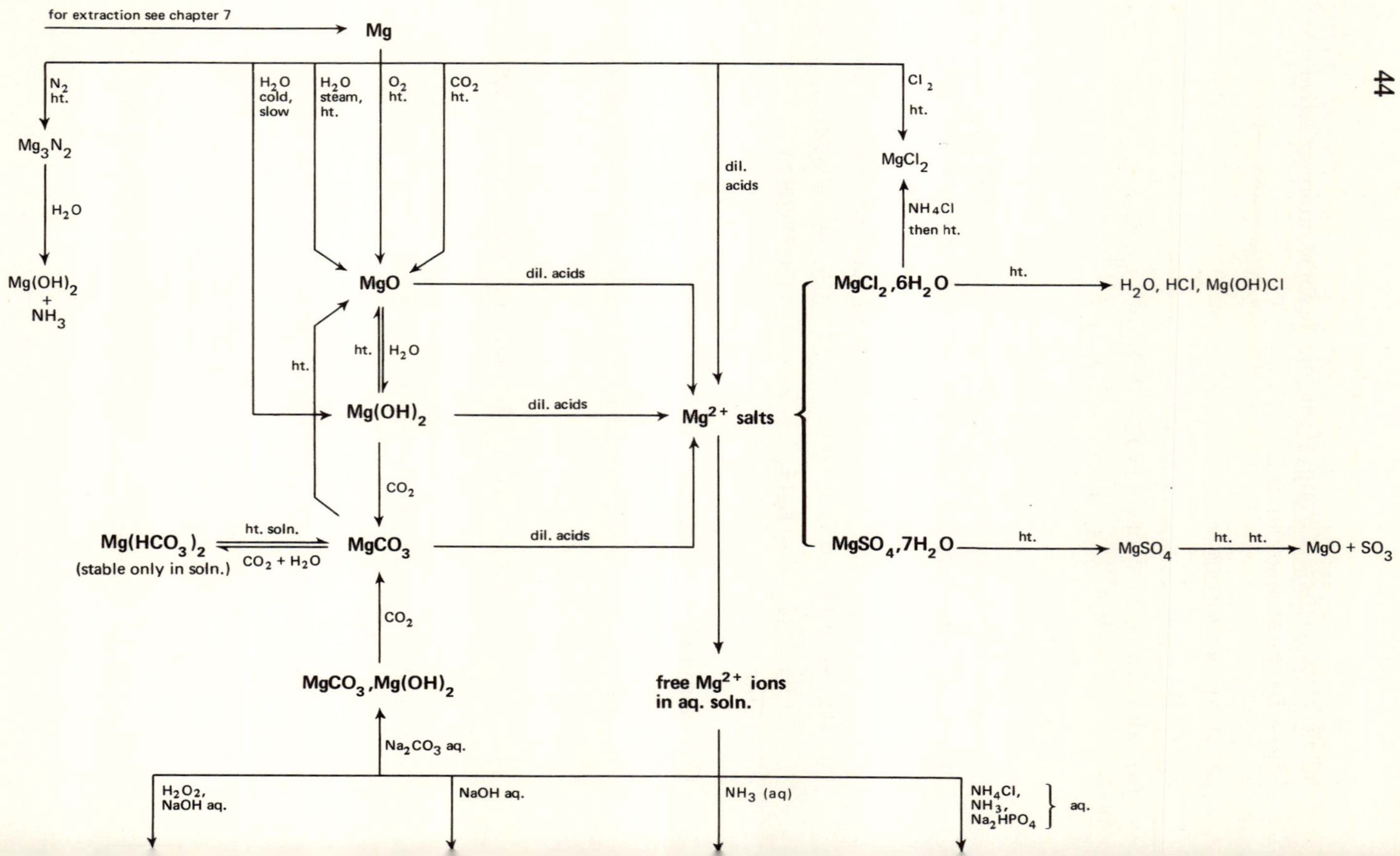

for extraction see chapter 7

Mg

N_2 ht. → Mg_3N_2 → H_2O → $Mg(OH)_2$ + NH_3

H_2O cold, slow

H_2O steam, ht.

O_2 ht.

CO_2 ht.

Cl_2 ht. → $MgCl_2$ ← NH_4Cl then ht.

dil. acids →

MgO ⇌ (H_2O / ht.) **Mg(OH)₂** → CO_2 → **MgCO₃** ← CO_2 ← **MgCO₃·Mg(OH)₂**

ht.

dil. acids

dil. acids

dil. acids

Mg²⁺ salts

$\{$ **MgCl₂·6H₂O** ht. → H_2O, HCl, Mg(OH)Cl

MgSO₄·7H₂O ht. → $MgSO_4$ ht. ht. → $MgO + SO_3$ $\}$

free Mg²⁺ ions in aq. soln.

Mg(HCO₃)₂ (stable only in soln.) ⇌ ht. soln. / $CO_2 + H_2O$

Na_2CO_3 aq.

H_2O_2, NaOH aq.

NaOH aq.

NH_3 (aq)

$\{$ NH₄Cl, NH₃, Na₂HPO₄ $\}$ aq.

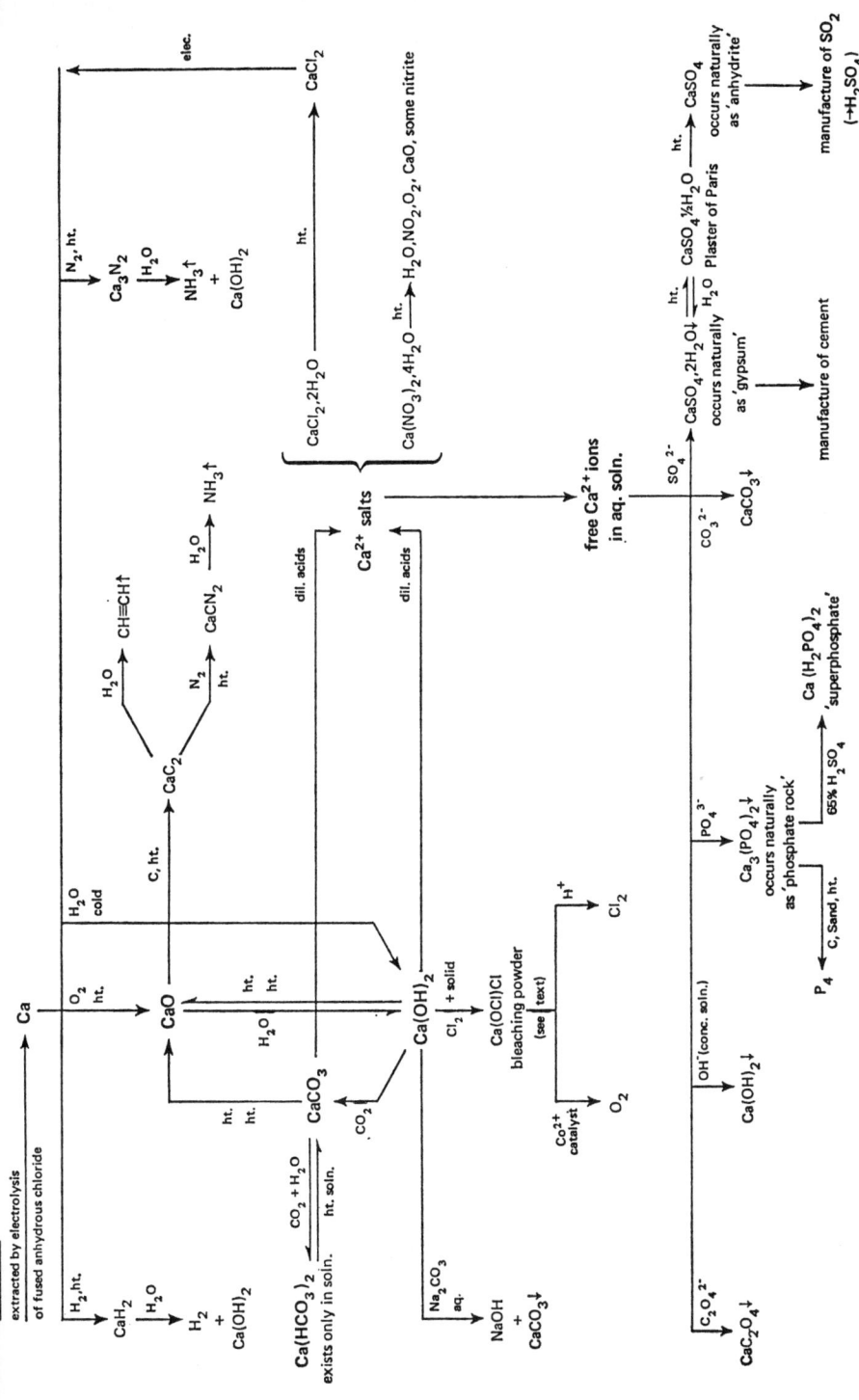

are sparingly soluble in water but that of Mg (Epsom salts $MgSO_4,7H_2O$) is readily soluble.

(b) The carbonates dissociate when strongly heated (e.g. in a lime kiln)

$$CaCO_3 \rightleftharpoons CaO + CO_2$$

(c) Hydrogen carbonates are formed (as in Group I) but exist only in solution. Heating the solution yields CO_2 and a precipitate of the carbonate

$$CaCO_3 + CO_2 + H_2O \rightleftharpoons Ca(HCO_3)_2$$

(d) All alkaline earth compounds give flame colorations: Ca—brick red; Sr—crimson; Ba—apple green.

SECTION D
GROUP III: BORON and ALUMINIUM

	Atomic number	Electronic configuration of atoms
B	5	2, 3
Al	13	2, 8, 3

Atoms of both elements contain three electrons more than those of the noble gases.

Boron has an extremely small atomic radius (see p. 5) and the energy required to remove three electrons from the powerful attraction of the nucleus is so great that the B^{3+} ion is not formed. In consequence, boron exhibits almost completely non-metallic character; its oxide is acidic, it forms oxyacids, and its chloride BCl_3 is liquid and is readily hydrolysed.

Aluminium, with its larger atom, can lose three electrons to form the Al^{3+} ion. The element is metallic, but it does exhibit some non-metallic character; its oxide is amphoteric and its anhydrous chloride is largely covalent (though solid) and it fumes in contact with air.

CHEMICAL PROPERTIES

Elements

Aluminium appears to be far less reactive than one would expect from its position in the E.C.S., and this is due to its ability to form a very thin but extremely coherent and inert oxide layer. It is normally unaffected by air, water or nitric acid. If, however, the metal surface is amalgamated, e.g. by dipping into a solution of a mercury(II) salt

$$3Hg^{2+} + 2Al \longrightarrow 2Al^{3+} + 3Hg$$

this prevents the adhesion of the oxide layer; attack by air is then extremely rapid

$$4Al + 3O_2 \longrightarrow 2Al_2O_3$$

as also is the displacement of hydrogen from water

$$2Al + 6H_2O \longrightarrow 2Al(OH)_3 + 3H_2$$

Aluminium is little attacked by dilute sulphuric acid (a layer of insoluble basic sulphate being formed) but rapidly dissolves in hydrochloric acid

$$2Al + 6HCl \longrightarrow 2AlCl_3 + 3H_2$$

Boron and aluminium both react with caustic alkalis

$$B + 2OH^- \text{ (fused alkali)} \longrightarrow H_2 + BO_2^- \text{ (metaborate)}$$
$$Al + 2OH^- \text{ (aq. alkali)} \longrightarrow H_2 + AlO_2^- \text{ (meta-aluminate)}$$

Oxides and hydroxides

Al_2O_3 and $Al(OH)_3$ are amphoteric

$$Al_2O_3 + 6HCl \longrightarrow 2AlCl_3 + 3H_2O$$
$$Al_2O_3 + 2NaOH \longrightarrow 2NaAlO_2 + H_2O$$

If aluminium oxide is heated strongly or left in contact with water for a long time it becomes highly resistant to attack by acids and alkalis.

B_2O_3 is acidic, forming orthoboric acid with excess water and metaborate with caustic alkali

$$B_2O_3 + 3H_2O \longrightarrow 2H_3BO_3$$
$$B_2O_3 + 2NaOH \longrightarrow 2NaBO_2 + H_2O$$

Orthoboric acid, H_3BO_3, or $B(OH)_3$, is a very weak acid.

Other compounds

Aluminium salts contain the colourless Al^{3+} ion, usually heavily hydrated as $Al(H_2O)_6{}^{3+}$. Aqueous solutions are strongly acid as a result of hydrolysis; this may take place in stages

$$Al(H_2O)_6{}^{3+} + H_2O \rightleftharpoons Al(OH)(H_2O)_5{}^{2+} + H_3O^+$$
$$Al(OH)(H_2O)_5{}^{2+} + H_2O \rightleftharpoons Al(OH)_2(H_2O)_4{}^+ + H_3O^+$$
$$Al(OH)_2(H_2O)_4{}^+ + H_2O \rightleftharpoons Al(OH)_3(H_2O)_3 + H_3O^+$$
$$\text{hydrated aluminium}$$
$$\text{oxide}$$

Similar behaviour is noted with tin and lead salts and those of the transition metals.

Boron forms no salts.

(a) Chlorides

BCl_3 is a colourless, covalent liquid which is completely hydrolysed by water

$$BCl_3 + 3H_2O \longrightarrow H_3BO_3 + 3HCl$$

$AlCl_3$, anhydrous, is largely covalent, fuming in moist air as a result of hydrolysis

$$AlCl_3 + 3H_2O \rightleftharpoons Al(OH)_3 + 3HCl$$

It sublimes at 180°C and in the vapour phase exists as the dimer Al_2Cl_6.

(b) Alums

These are double sulphates of unipositive metal ions (e.g. K^+, Na^+, $NH_4{}^+$) and tripositive metal ions (e.g. Fe^{3+}, Cr^{3+}, Al^{3+}) of formula

$$M_2^I SO_4, M_2^{III}(SO_4)_3, 24H_2O$$

(*Continued on page 50*)

ALUMINIUM

for extraction see chapter 7

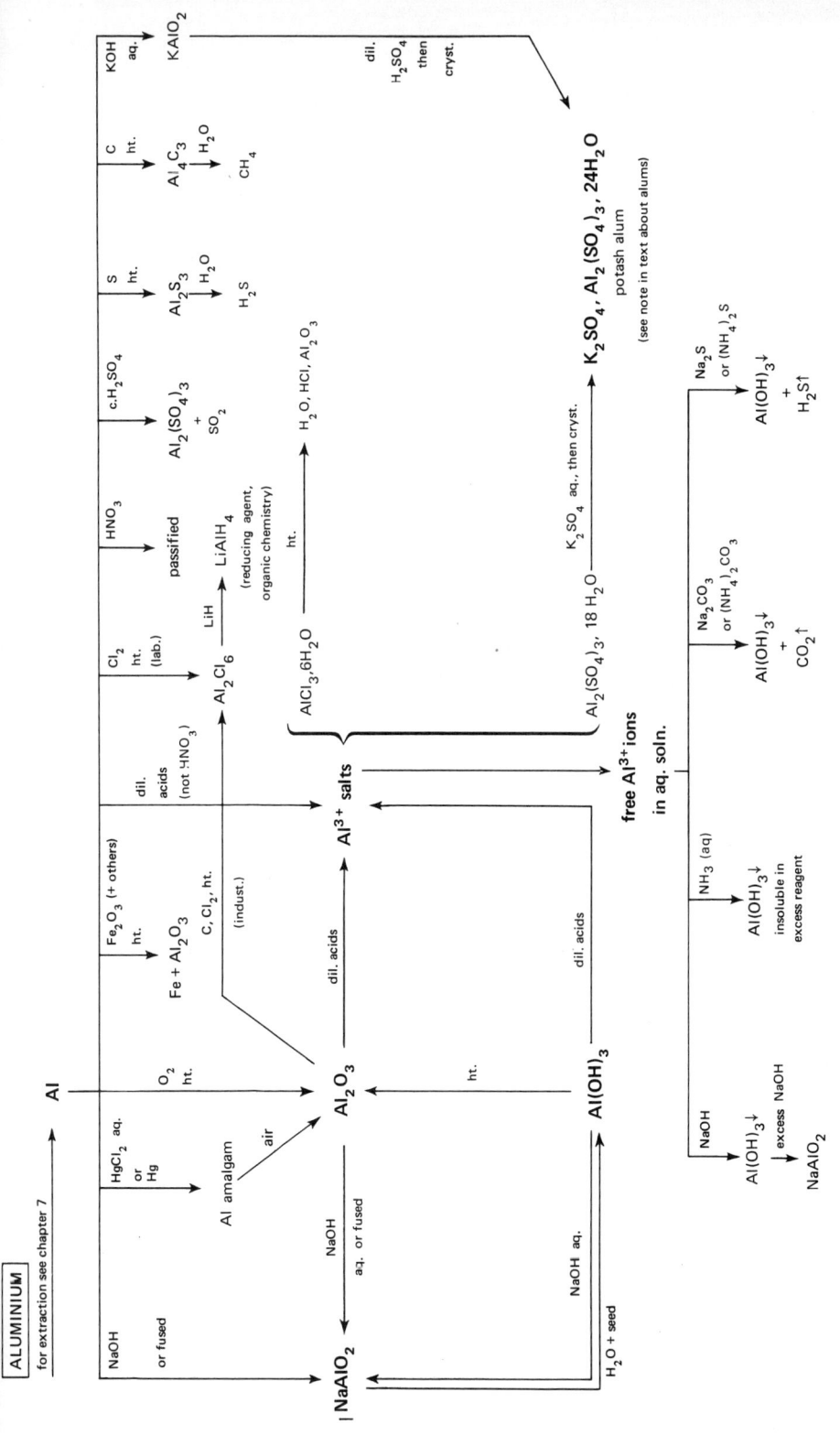

They are isomorphous, crystallise in octahedra, and they are typical double salts—see p. 22.

Common examples are

potash alum $\qquad$ $K_2SO_4,Al_2(SO_4)_3,24H_2O$
ammonium iron(III) alum $\quad (NH_4)_2SO_4,Fe_2(SO_4)_3,24H_2O$
chrome alum $\qquad$ $K_2SO_4,Cr_2(SO_4)_3,24H_2O$

SECTION E
GROUP IV: CARBON, SILICON, Germanium, TIN and LEAD

	Atomic number	Electronic configuration of atoms
C	6	2, 4
Si	14	2, 8, 4
Ge	32	2, 8, 18, 4
Sn	50	2, 8, 18, 18, 4
Pb	82	2, 8, 18, 32, 18, 4

Atoms of all the elements in this group contain four electrons in their outer shells (i.e. four less than the noble gas configurations). All exhibit tetracovalence, but this becomes less important as atomic radius increases $C \rightarrow Pb$. However, increasing atomic radius makes ion formation easier and both Sn and Pb are able to form M^{2+} and M^{4+} ions. Sn^{4+} is more stable than Sn^{2+} (the latter is powerfully reducing) but Pb^{2+} is more stable than the strongly oxidising Pb^{4+}—the common lead salts contain the Pb^{2+} ion.

The changes down the group, $C \rightarrow Pb$, may be summarised:

(i) There is a change from non-metallic to metallic character.

(ii) The covalence of four becomes less important and is unimportant in lead.

(iii) The electrovalence of two, absent in C and Si, becomes more stable and is in fact the more stable valency with lead.

CHEMICAL PROPERTIES

These are summarised and compared in the table on pp. 52 and 53.

ALLOTROPY

Of carbon

Allotropes: graphite, diamond.

Type of allotropy: monotropic (see p. 15), graphite being the stable variety under ordinary conditions (though of course diamond is also very stable) as indicated by thermochemical data.

Structures: graphite has a hexagonal, layer structure with weak van der Waals forces between layers (good lubricant, good electrical conductor); diamond has a compact, three dimensional, tetrahedral structure (giant molecule); other forms of carbon (e.g. charcoals) have deformed graphitic structures.

Of tin

Allotropes: grey, white, rhombic
Type of allotropy: enantiotropic (see p. 15), the transition temperatures being

$$\text{grey} \overset{18°C}{\rightleftharpoons} \text{white} \overset{170°C}{\rightleftharpoons} \text{rhombic (m.p. 232°C)}$$

White tin is the stable allotrope under normal conditions; the change white → grey is very slow and only measurable well below 18°C.

Elements	Carbon	Silicon	Tin	Lead
General	non-metallic, but graphite conducts electricity	non-metallic	metallic	metallic
Oxidation states	$+4$	$+4$	$+2$ powerfully reducing $+4$, more stable	$+2$, more stable $+4$, often unstable, oxidising
Ht. strongly in excess air	forms gaseous dioxide CO_2	forms white solid dioxide, $(SiO_2)_n$, silica (giant molecule)	forms white tin(IV) oxide, SnO_2	forms orange-pink monoxide PbO, litharge
Effect of conc. HNO_3	gives highest oxide, heat required $C + 4HNO_3 \rightarrow$ $CO_2 + 4NO_2 + 2H_2O$	no reaction	gives hydrated tin(IV) oxide, $SnO_2.xH_2O$ $Sn + 4HNO_3 \rightarrow$ $SnO_2 + 4NO_2 + 2H_2O$	oxidised to a salt—lead(II) nitrate $Pb + 4HNO_3 \rightarrow$ $Pb(NO_3)_2 + 2NO_2 + 2H_2O$
Effect of conc. H_2SO_4	gives highest oxide, heat required $C + 2H_2SO_4 \rightarrow$ $CO_2 + 2SO_2 + 2H_2O$	no reaction	gives salt, mainly tin(IV) $Sn + 4H_2SO_4 \rightarrow$ $Sn(SO_4)_2 + 2SO_2 + 2H_2O$	gives lead(II) salt $Pb + 2H_2SO_4 \rightarrow$ $PbSO_4 + SO_2 + 2H_2O$ (main reaction)
Effect of dil. acids	no reaction	no reaction	gives tin(II) salt and hydrogen $Sn + 2H^+ \rightarrow Sn^{2+} + H_2$	very slow, gives lead(II) salt and hydrogen $Pb + 2H^+ \rightarrow Pb^{2+} + H_2$
Effect of alkali	no reaction	silicate and hydrogen formed $Si + 2OH^- + H_2O \rightarrow$ $SiO_3^{2-} + 2H_2$	stannate(II) and hydrogen formed $Sn + 2OH^- \rightarrow$ $SnO_2^{2-} + H_2$	very slow, plumbate(II) and hydrogen formed $Pb + 2OH^- \rightarrow$ $PbO_2^{2-} + H_2$
Oxides **Dioxides**	CO_2, gas, acidic, moderately soluble in water $CO_2 + H_2O \rightleftharpoons H_2CO_3$ with alkali: $CO_2 + 2OH^- \rightarrow$ $CO_3^{2-} + H_2O$ then $CO_2 + CO_3^{2-} + H_2O \rightarrow$ $2HCO_3^-$	SiO_2, white, solid, acidic, giant molecule, insol. in water; with alkali: $SiO_2 + 2OH^- \rightarrow$ $SiO_3^{2-} + H_2O$ silicate ion is polymer $[SiO_3^{2-}]_x$	SnO_2, white, solid, amphoteric, insol. in water $SnO_2 + 2H_2SO_4 (conc.) \rightarrow$ $Sn(SO_4)_2 + 2H_2O$ $SnO_2 + 2OH^- \rightarrow$ $SnO_3^{2-} + H_2O$ (stannate(IV))	PbO_2, dark-brown solid, insol. in water, amphoteric $PbO_2 + 4HCl \rightarrow$ $PbCl_4 + 2H_2O$ (ice-cold) see below for HCl at higher temp. $PbO_2 + 2OH^-$ (conc. aq.) $\rightarrow$ $PbO_3^{2-} + H_2O$ (plumbate(IV))

Monoxides	CO, gas, neutral, burns to CO_2 in air	SiO, brown solid, oxidised by air at room temp. $2SiO + O_2 \rightarrow 2SiO_2$ powerful reducing agent	SnO, dark-brown solid, smoulders to SnO_2 in air, amphoteric $SnO + 2H^+ \rightarrow Sn^{2+} + H_2O$ $SnO + 2OH^- \rightarrow SnO_2^{2-} + H_2O$ (stannate(II))	PbO, yellow (often pinkish), solid, stable oxide of lead, amphoteric $PbO + 2H^+ \rightarrow Pb^{2+} + H_2O$ $PbO + 2OH^- \rightarrow PbO_2^{2-} + H_2O$ (plumbate(II))
Other Compounds **Chlorides**	CCl_4, liquid, very stable, only covalent chloride which is not hydrolysed	$SiCl_4$, colourless covalent liquid readily hydrolysed $SiCl_4 + 2H_2O \rightarrow SiO_2 + 4HCl$	$SnCl_4$, colourless covalent liquid, fumes in air, readily hydrolysed: $SnCl_4 + 2H_2O \rightarrow SnO_2 + 4HCl$ aq. soln. also contains $Sn(H_2O)_6^{4+}$ and Cl^- $SnCl_2, 2H_2O$, white cryst., reducing agent, hydrolysed $SnCl_2 + 2H_2O \rightleftharpoons Sn(OH)Cl + HCl$	$PbCl_4$, yellow covalent liquid, thermally unstable at room temperature $PbCl_4 \rightarrow PbCl_2 + Cl_2$ and readily hydrolysed: $PbCl_4 + 2H_2O \rightarrow PbO_2 + 4HCl$ $PbCl_2$, ionic, white, stable chloride of lead, sparingly soluble in cold water, readily soluble in hot water.
Hydrides	vast number, covalent, stable, burn in air, e.g. $CH_4 + 2O_2 \rightarrow CO_2 + 2H_2O$	many, covalent, gases and liquids, spontaneously inflammable in air, e.g. $SiH_4 + 2O_2 \rightarrow SiO_2 + 2H_2O$	SnH_4 only, covalent gas, unstable at room temperature	PbH_4, very unstable, covalent
Sulphides	CS_2, colourless, covalent, liquid, very inflammable in air $CS_2 + 3O_2 \rightarrow CO_2 + 2SO_2$	SiS_2, white needles, hydrolysed $SiS_2 + 2H_2O \rightarrow SiO_2 + 2H_2S$	SnS_2, yellow, SnS brown, both insol. in water, pptd. by H_2S from acid soln.; both sol. in yellow ammonium sulphide $SnS_2 + S^{2-} \rightarrow SnS_3^{2-} + S$ $SnS + S^{2-} \rightarrow SnS_3^{2-}$ (thiostannate(IV))	PbS only, black, insol. in water, pptd. by H_2S in acid solution, insoluble in yellow ammonium sulphide

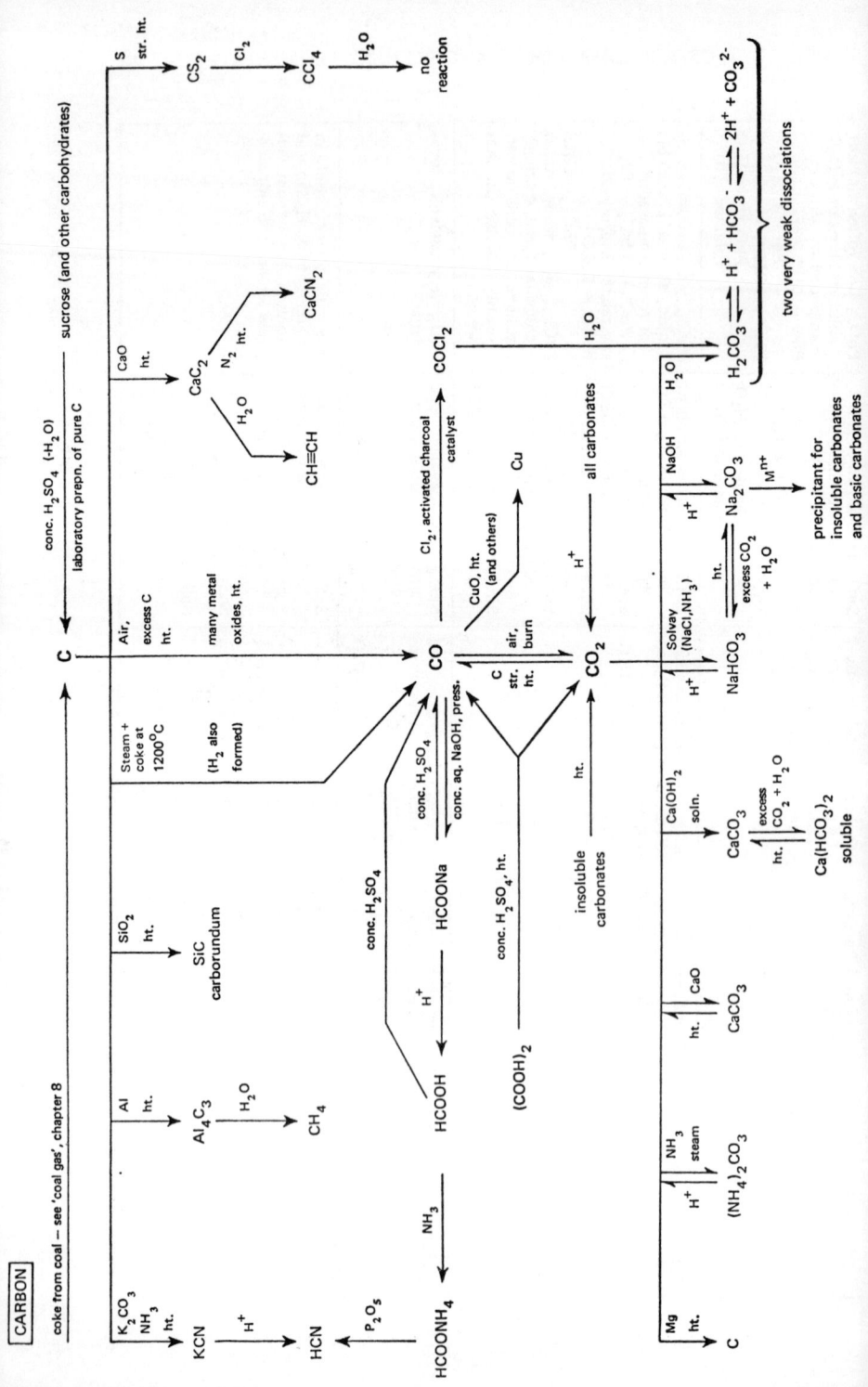

CARBON

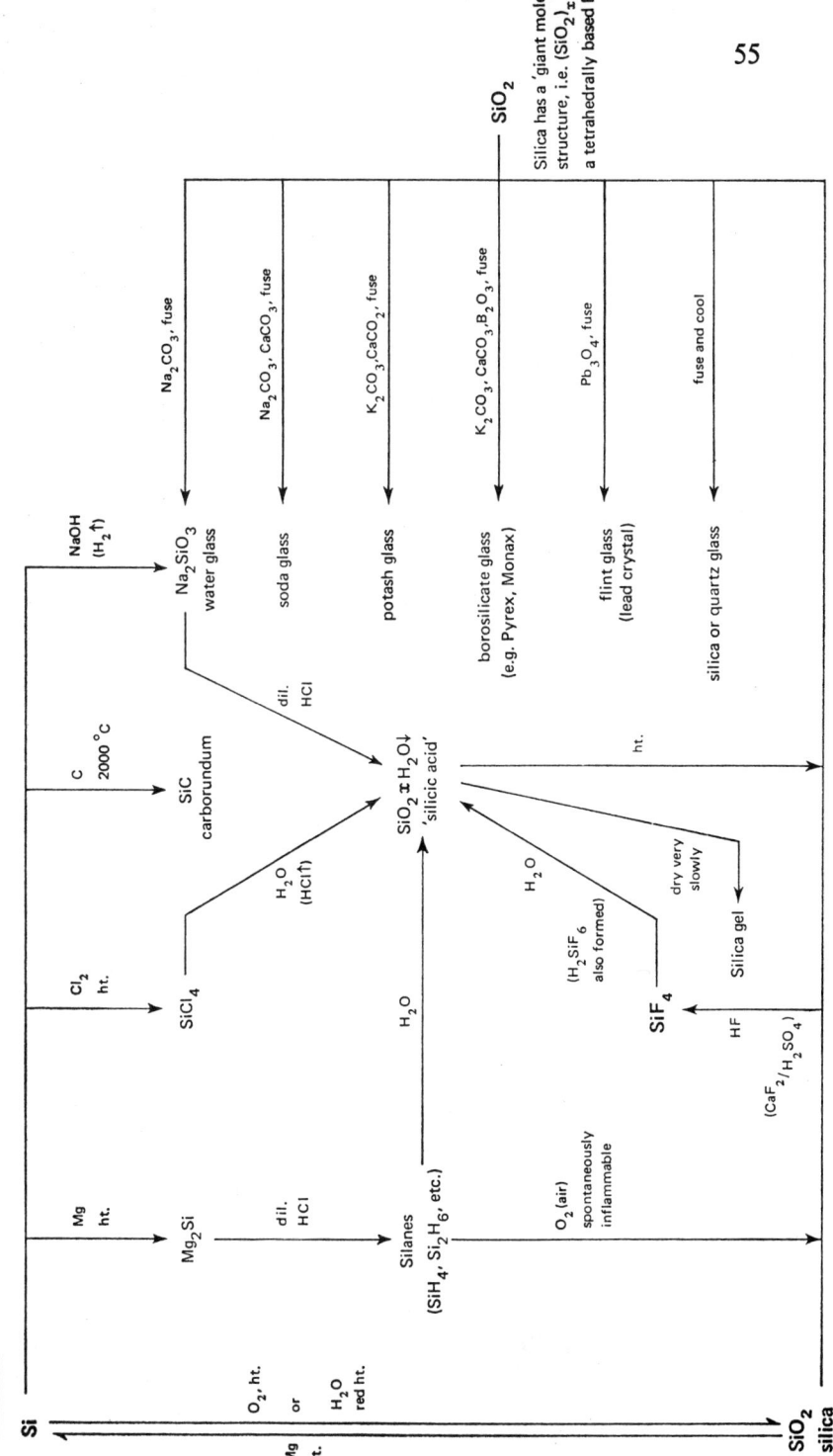

SILICON

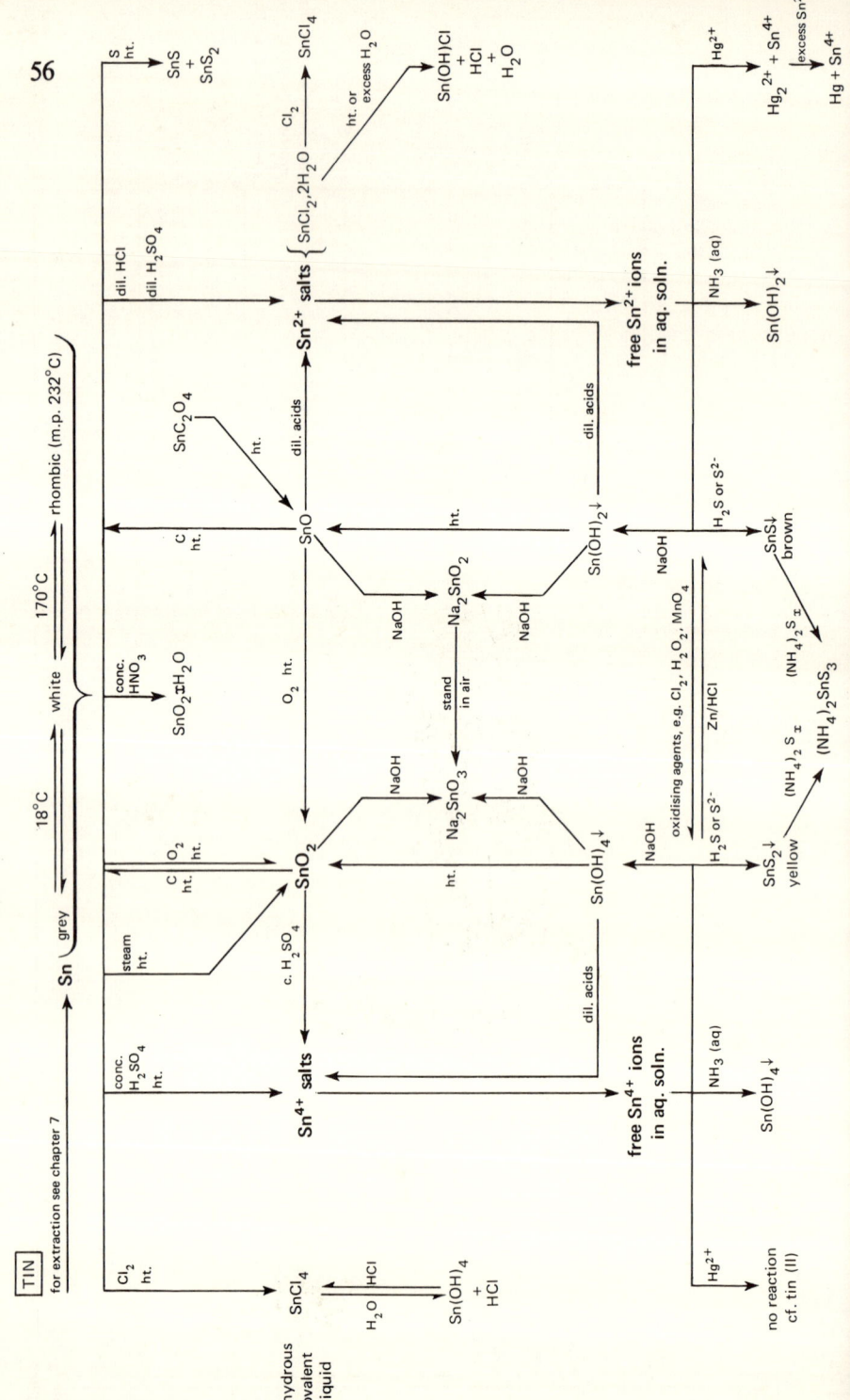

TIN

for extraction see chapter 7

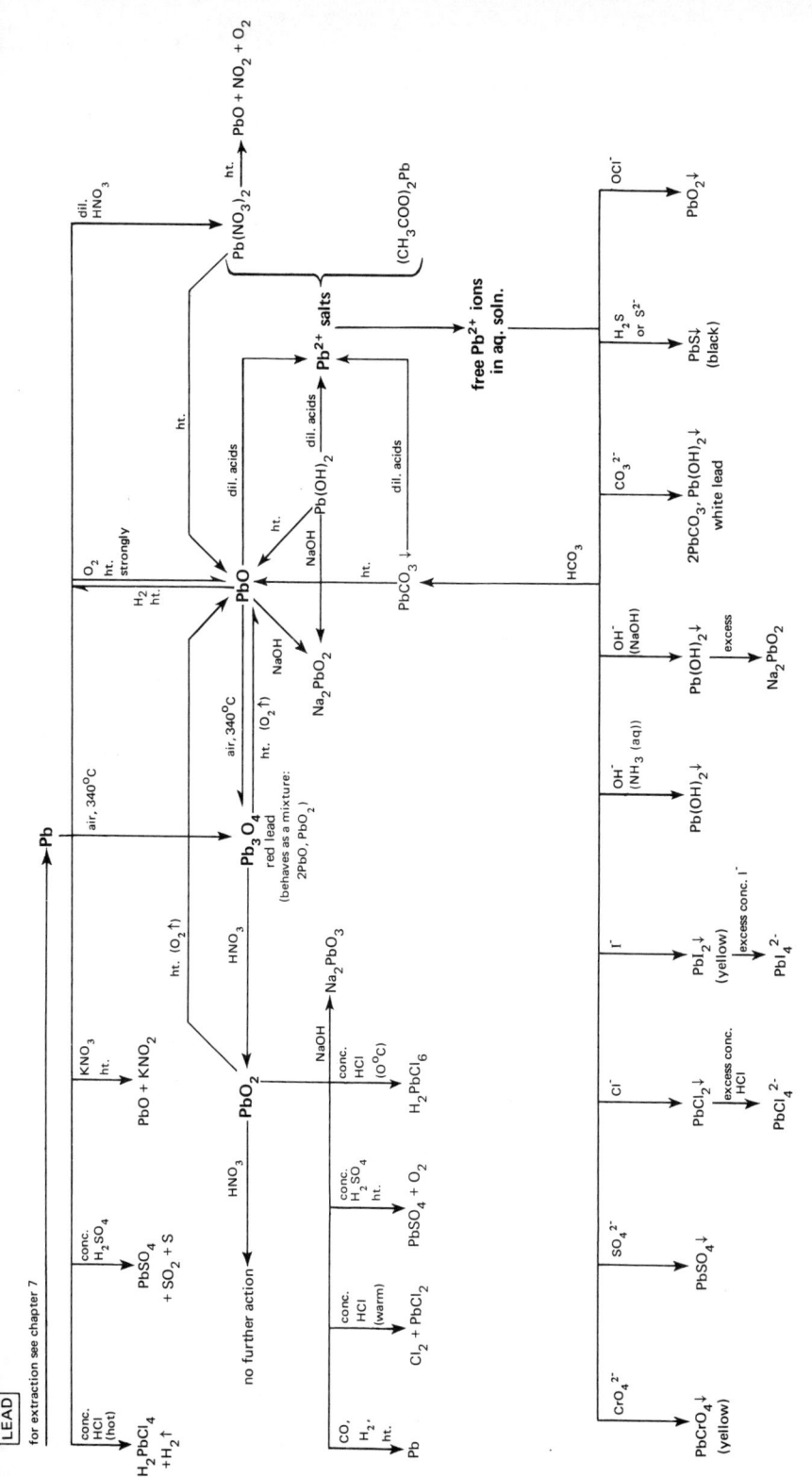

LEAD

for extraction see chapter 7

SECTION F
GROUP V: NITROGEN, PHOSPHORUS, ARSENIC, ANTIMONY and BISMUTH

	Atomic number	Electronic configuration of atoms
N	7	2, 5
P	15	2, 8, 5
As	33	2, 8, 18, 5
Sb	51	2, 8, 18, 18, 5
Bi	83	2, 8, 18, 32, 18, 5

Atoms of these elements contain five electrons in their valency shells—three fewer than the nearest noble gas.

Nitrogen differs somewhat from other members of the group on account of

(a) its very small atomic radius and

(b) its valency shell (L) having a capacity limited to eight electrons.

With a small atomic radius it has a great tendency to attract electrons into its valency shell, and it is the only element to form a trinegative ion (N^{3-}). Also, since its valency shell is only able to accommodate eight electrons, pentacovalence is impossible since this would require ten electrons (i.e. five pairs) in this shell; thus nitrogen forms no compounds comparable with PCl_5, H_3PO_3, etc. Nitrogen exhibits tricovalence in common with other elements of the group, e.g. NH_3.

As in Group IV (p. 50), the increasing atomic radius as the group is descended results in

(a) a change from non-metallic properties (N, P) to metallic (Bi) via As and Sb which could be described as 'metalloids', i.e. possessing both metallic and non-metallic properties;

(b) the higher valency (5) becoming less stable and the lower valency (3) more stable. With increasing stability of the trivalent state the tendency to form tripositive ions M^{3+} also becomes greater.

CHEMICAL PROPERTIES

These are summarised and compared in the table on p. 60. In addition the student should note that, in descending the group,

(i) the covalent hydrides become less stable;

(ii) the oxides change from acidic (N, P) → amphoteric (As, Sb) → basic (Bi);

(iii) only Sb and Bi can form salts with oxyacids;

(iv) the trichlorides become more ionic and thus (a) the extent to which they are hydrolysed decreases and (b) the m.ps. increase.

ALLOTROPY OF PHOSPHORUS

Allotropes: yellow (or white), red (or violet).

Type of allotropy: monotropic (see p. 15), red being the stable variety. Yellow changes to red slowly at room temperature and much more rapidly at elevated temperatures, particularly with iodine as catalyst (see p. 115). Red is converted to yellow by strongly heating to vaporise and then cooling rapidly, e.g. by passing into water.

The principal differences between yellow and red phosphorus are given in the following table:

Yellow	Red
Soluble in carbon disulphide	Insoluble
Poisonous	Non-poisonous
Ignites readily in air (so kept under water)	Stable in air at room temperature (so no special storage precautions)
Low m.p. (44°C)	High m.p. (590°C under pressure)
Phosphoresces (glows) in air	Does not glow in air
Reacts with conc. aqueous alkali on heating $P_4 + 3OH^- + 3H_2O \rightarrow$ $PH_3 + 3H_2PO_2^-$	No reaction

	Nitrogen	Phosphorus	Arsenic	Antimony	Bismuth
Elements General	non-metal (colourless gas)	non-metal	metalloid	metalloid	metal
Comparative stability of principal oxidation states	+5 more stable than +3	as for nitrogen	+5 and +3 of comparable stability	+3 more stable than +5	+3 stable, +5 uncommon and strongly oxidising
Heat in excess air	forms NO at very high temperature	forms P_4O_{10}	forms As_4O_6	forms mainly Sb_4O_6	forms Bi_2O_3
Effect of conc. nitric acid	no action	forms orthophosphoric acid $P_4 + 20HNO_3 \rightarrow 4H_3PO_4 + 20NO_2 + 4H_2O$	similar to phosphorus—forms H_3AsO_4	forms Sb_2O_5	forms the nitrate $Bi(NO_3)_3$
Effect of conc. sulphuric acid	no action	forms orthophosphoric acid	forms arsenious acid H_3AsO_3	forms the sulphate $Sb_2(SO_4)_3$	forms the sulphate $Bi_2(SO_4)_3$
Oxides	neutral: N_2O, NO acidic: $N_2O_3 + H_2O \rightarrow 2HNO_2$ $N_2O_4 + H_2O \rightarrow HNO_2 + HNO_3$ $N_2O_5 + H_2O \rightarrow 2HNO_3$	acidic: P_4O_6, P_4O_{10} $P_4O_6 + 6H_2O \rightarrow 4H_3PO_3$ $P_4O_{10} + 6H_2O \rightarrow 4H_3PO_4$	amphoteric: As_4O_6 $As_4O_6 + 6H_2O \rightarrow 4H_3AsO_3$ $As_4O_6 + 12HCl \rightarrow 4AsCl_3 + 6H_2O$ acidic: As_2O_5 $As_2O_5 + 3H_2O \rightarrow 2H_3AsO_4$	amphoteric: Sb_4O_6 acidic: Sb_2O_5 as for oxides of arsenic	basic: Bi_2O_3 $Bi_2O_3 + 6HCl \rightarrow 2BiCl_3 + 3H_2O$
Other compounds Trichlorides	NCl_3, highly explosive, yellow covalent liquid; unusual hydrolysis $NCl_3 + 3H_2O \rightleftharpoons NH_3 + 3HOCl$	PCl_3, colourless, fuming covalent liquid; readily hydrolysed $PCl_3 + 3H_2O \rightarrow 2H_3PO_3 + 3HCl$	$AsCl_3$, colourless, fuming covalent liquid; hydrolysis reversible $4AsCl_3 + 6H_2O \rightleftharpoons As_4O_6 + 12HCl$	$SbCl_3$, white solid; hydrolysis reversible and stepwise $SbCl_3 + H_2O \rightleftharpoons SbOCl + 2HCl$ $4SbOCl + 2H_2O \rightleftharpoons Sb_4O_6 + 4HCl$	$BiCl_3$, white solid; reversible hydrolysis to oxychloride only $BiCl_3 + H_2O \rightleftharpoons BiOCl + 2HCl$

Pentachlorides	not formed	PCl_5, white solid (structure is PCl_4^+, PCl_6^-), fuming in moist air; vapour is $PCl_5 \rightleftharpoons PCl_3 + Cl_2$; readily hydrolysed: $PCl_5 + 4H_2O \rightarrow H_3PO_4 + 5HCl$	not formed	$SbCl_5$, yellow, fuming covalent liquid; readily hydrolysed: $2SbCl_5 + 5H_2O \rightarrow Sb_2O_5 + 10HCl$	not formed
Oxyacids	HNO_3 strong; oxidising HNO_2 weak; only in aq. soln. (none corresponding to H_3PO_4, H_3PO_3, etc.; 8 being max. no. of electrons in valency shell of N)	all weak: H_3PO_4 H_3PO_3 reducing agent H_3PO_2 strong reducing agent	all weak: H_3AsO_3—only in aqueous soln. H_3AsO_4—weakly oxidising	existence doubtful	not formed
Trihydrides	NH_3, gas, base of weak to moderate strength: $NH_3 + H_2O \rightleftharpoons NH_4^+ + OH^-$ salts stable under normal conditions, but break down on heating; NH_3 decomposed to N_2 and H_2 on prolonged sparking	PH_3, gas, feebly basic: $PH_3 + HI \rightarrow PH_4I$ salt of reasonable stability in absence of water; PH_3 decomposed to P_4 and H_2 at elevated temperatures	AsH_3, neutral gas, readily decomposed on heating to As_4 and H_2	SbH_3, as for AsH_3 but decomposes more readily	BiH_3, extremely unstable neutral gas; only obtainable in traces

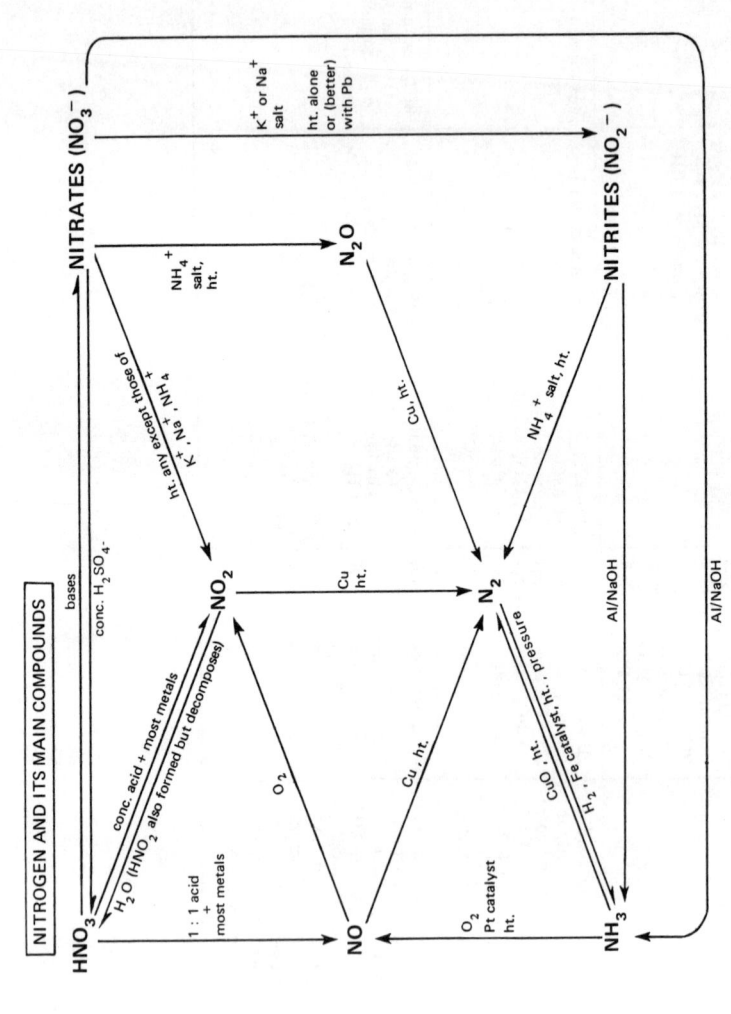

NITROGEN AND ITS MAIN COMPOUNDS

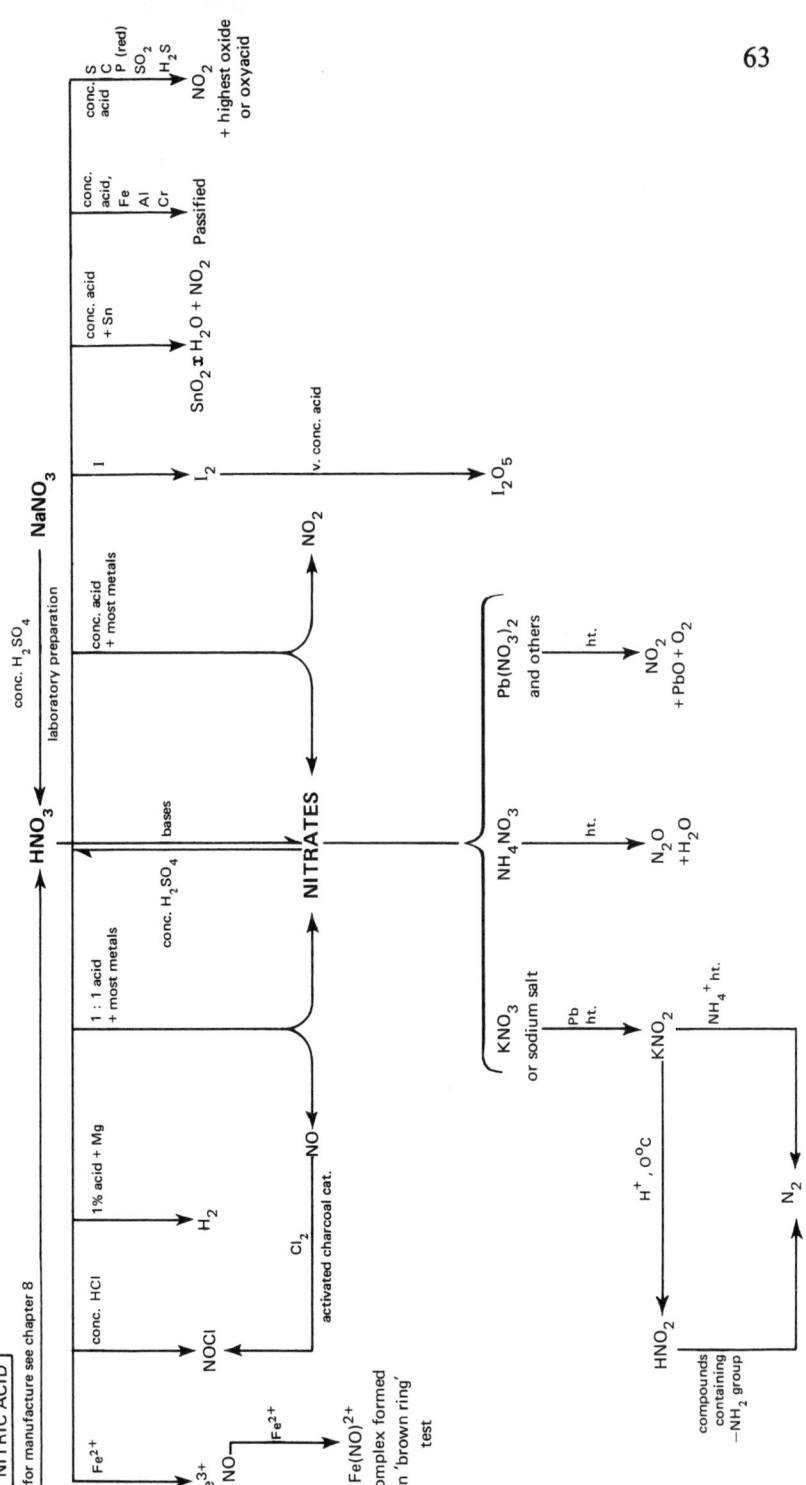

NITRIC ACID

for manufacture see chapter 8

HNO_3 conc. H_2SO_4 **NaNO_3**

laboratory preparation

Fe^{2+}

conc. HCl → NOCl

1% acid + Mg → H_2

1 : 1 acid + most metals

conc. H_2SO_4

bases

NITRATES

Fe^{3+} + NO

$Fe(NO)^{2+}$ complex formed in 'brown ring' test

Cl_2 activated charcoal cat. → NO

conc. acid + most metals → NO_2

I → I_2

v. conc. acid → I_2O_5

conc. acid + Sn → $SnO_2 \cdot x H_2O + NO_2$

conc. acid, Fe Al Cr → Passified

conc. S C acid P (red) SO_2 H_2S → NO_2 + highest oxide or oxyacid

KNO_3 or sodium salt

NH_4NO_3   ht. → $N_2O + H_2O$

Pb(NO_3)_2 and others   ht. → $NO_2 + PbO + O_2$

Pb ht. → KNO_2

H^+, 0°C → HNO_2

NH_4^+ ht. → N_2

compounds containing —NH_2 group → N_2

64

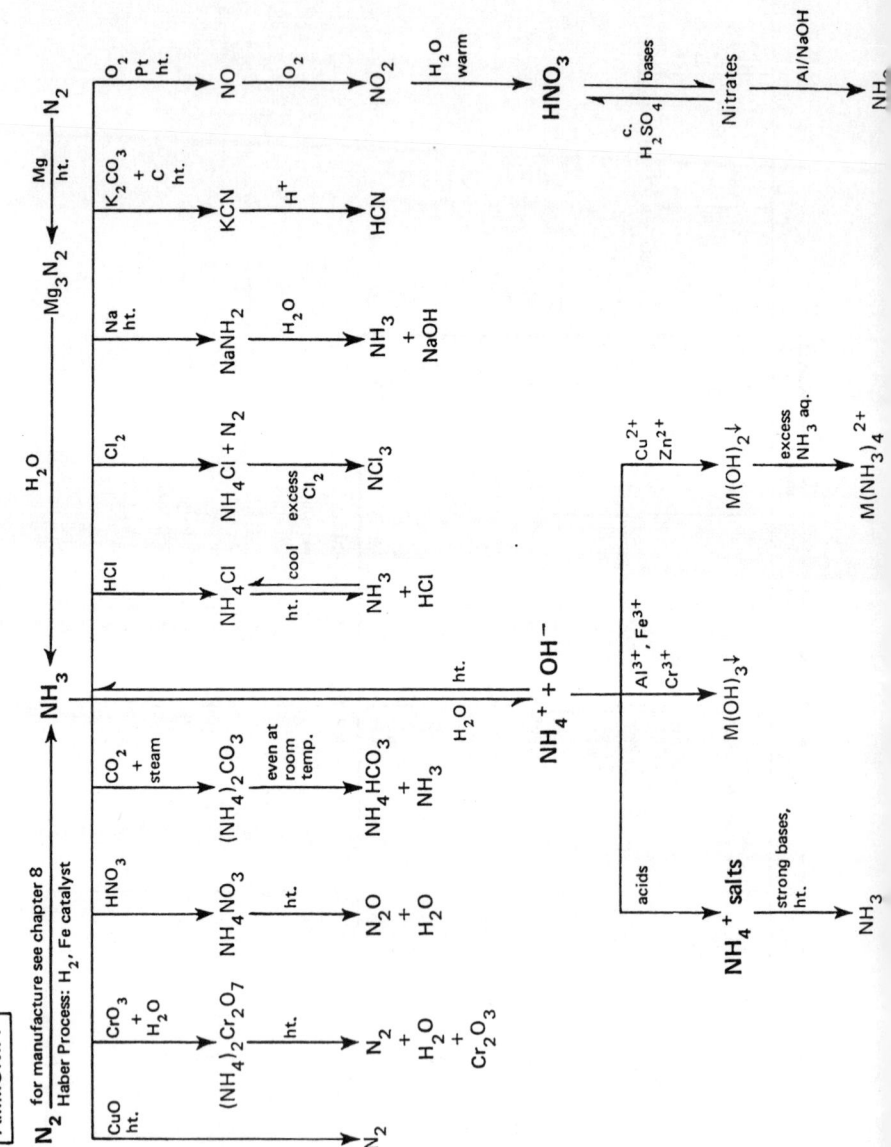

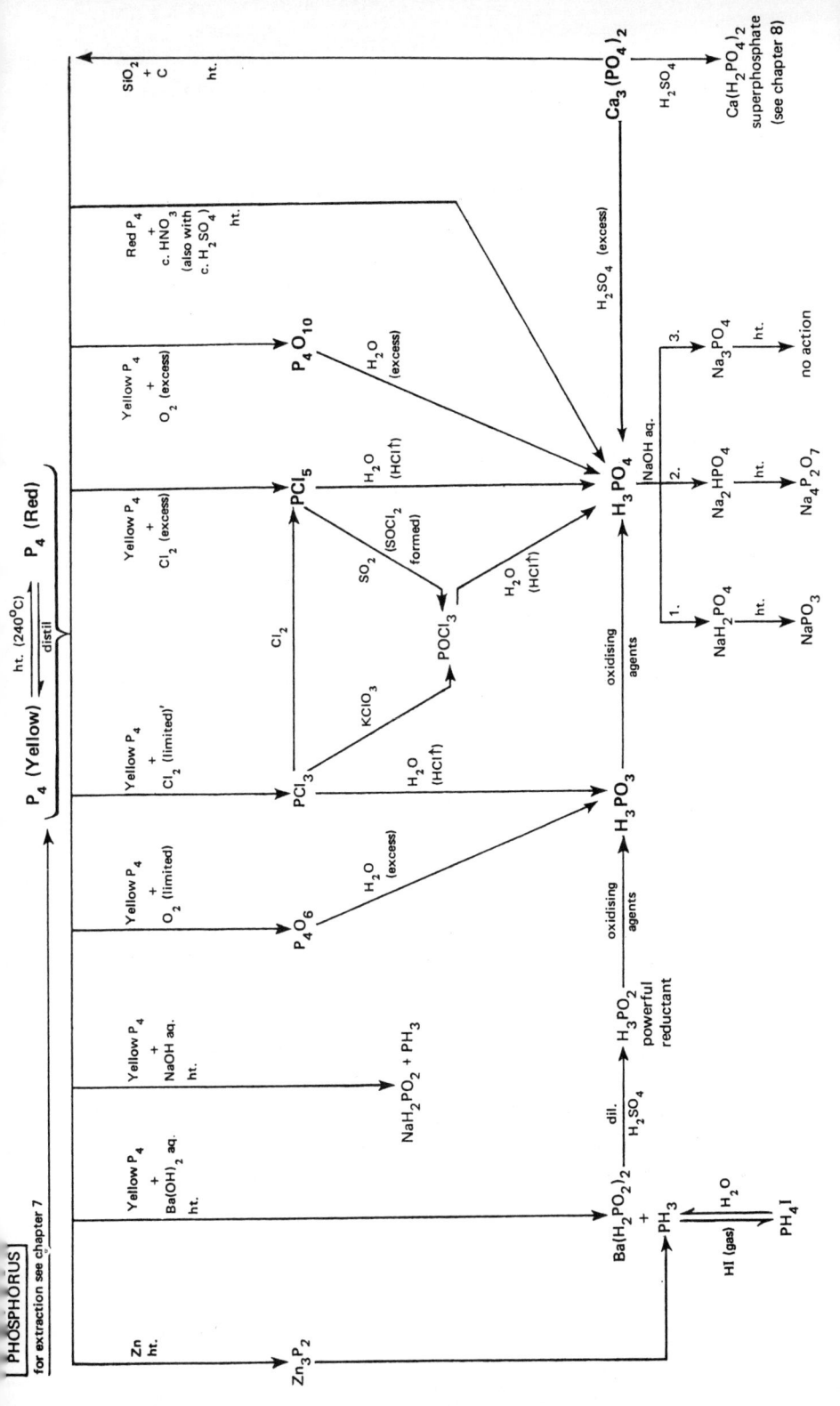

SECTION G
GROUP VI: OXYGEN and SULPHUR

	Atomic number	Electronic configuration of atoms
O	8	2, 6
S	16	2, 8, 6

Atoms of elements in this group contain six electrons in their outer shells, i.e. two fewer than the nearest noble gases.

The same trends occur as in Groups IV and V, i.e. as the group is descended and atomic radius increases the elements become more metallic. However, only oxygen and sulphur are at all common, and these are considered here.

Like nitrogen in the preceding group, the valency shell of oxygen cannot accommodate more than 8 electrons, and so oxygen does not exhibit the higher covalencies of 4 and 6 shown by sulphur. Similarities are thus restricted to the bivalent state, which may be electrovalent or covalent.

Both elements form binegative ions when reacting with the more electropositive elements, each atom gaining two electrons to achieve a noble gas configuration

$$X + 2e \longrightarrow X^{2-}$$

Oxide ions (O^{2-}) are formed more readily than sulphide ions (S^{2-}) since oxygen has a smaller atomic radius and electrons are more easily attracted into the valency shell which is closer to the nucleus.

The noble gas configurations may also be attained by covalent bond formation (one double or two single bonds). Comparable covalent compounds are H_2O and H_2S, CO_2 and CS_2. Sulphur may replace oxygen in many types of compound, e.g. ethers R—O—R and thioethers R—S—R, sulphates SO_4^{2-} and thiosulphates $S_2O_3^{2-}$.

OXIDES AND SULPHIDES OF METALS

These contain the ions O^{2-} and S^{2-} respectively. The majority of oxides and sulphides are only sparingly soluble in water. Those which are soluble (Group I and Group II metals) are considerably hydrolysed

$$O^{2-} + H_2O \longrightarrow 2OH^-$$
$$S^{2-} + H_2O \rightleftharpoons HS^- + OH^-$$
and $$HS^- + H_2O \rightleftharpoons H_2S + OH^-$$

Most sulphides (except those with very low solubility products, e.g. HgS) and all oxides of metals are soluble in dilute strong acids, the weak electrolytes hydrogen sulphide or water being produced

$$S^{2-} + 2H^+ \longrightarrow H_2S$$
$$O^{2-} + 2H^+ \longrightarrow H_2O$$

Oxides of metals are dealt with in greater detail on p. 17.

Many sulphides undergo aerial oxidation under suitable conditions. Gentle heating in air frequently yields a sulphate, e.g.

$$ZnS + 2O_2 \longrightarrow ZnSO_4$$

but at higher temperatures the metal oxide and sulphur dioxide are usually formed

$$2ZnS + 3O_2 \longrightarrow 2ZnO + 2SO_2$$

Use is made of these reactions in the extraction of several important metals (see Chapter 7).

HYDRIDES

These become less stable $O \rightarrow S$ as in Groups IV and V. The similarities are

(i) H_2O and H_2S are both weak electrolytes

$$H_2O \rightleftharpoons H^+ + OH^-$$
$$H_2S \rightleftharpoons H^+ + S^{2-}$$
$$HS^- \rightleftharpoons H^+ + S^{2-}$$

The great physical differences (e.g. b.p.) are due to the much greater electronegative character of oxygen and the consequent extensive hydrogen bonding in water.

(ii) Hydrogen peroxide (H_2O_2) and hydrogen disulphide (H_2S_2) have the same structure, i.e. H—X—X—H but H_2S_2 is much less stable than H_2O_2

$$2H_2O_2 \longrightarrow 2H_2O + O_2$$
$$H_2S_2 \longrightarrow H_2S + S$$

Both are liquids; H_2O_2 water-like, H_2S_2 a yellow oil.

ALLOTROPY

Of oxygen

There are two allotropes

diatomic gas, O_2 and   triatomic gas, O_3

Ozone is a highly endothermic species, and so its formation should be favoured by high temperatures. It is generally more convenient to supply energy in another form so that the allotrope may be prepared at lower temperatures, when it is more stable; a silent electric discharge is applied to diatomic oxygen.

Ozone is far more reactive than oxygen, e.g. it oxidises Hg, I^-, Fe^{2+} immediately on contact.

Of sulphur

In the solid state enantiotropic allotropy (see p. 15) is exhibited. The principal crystalline forms are

$$\text{Rhombic } (S_\alpha) \overset{96°C}{\rightleftharpoons} \text{Monoclinic } (S_\beta) \text{ m.p. } 120°C$$

In both these forms the molecular structure is S_8 rings. In the liquid state dynamic allotropy is exhibited.

The principal equilibria are

S_8 rings (S_λ) $\rightleftharpoons$ S_8, S_6, S_4 chains (S_π) $\rightleftharpoons$ S_n long chains (S_μ)

(*Continued on page 75*)

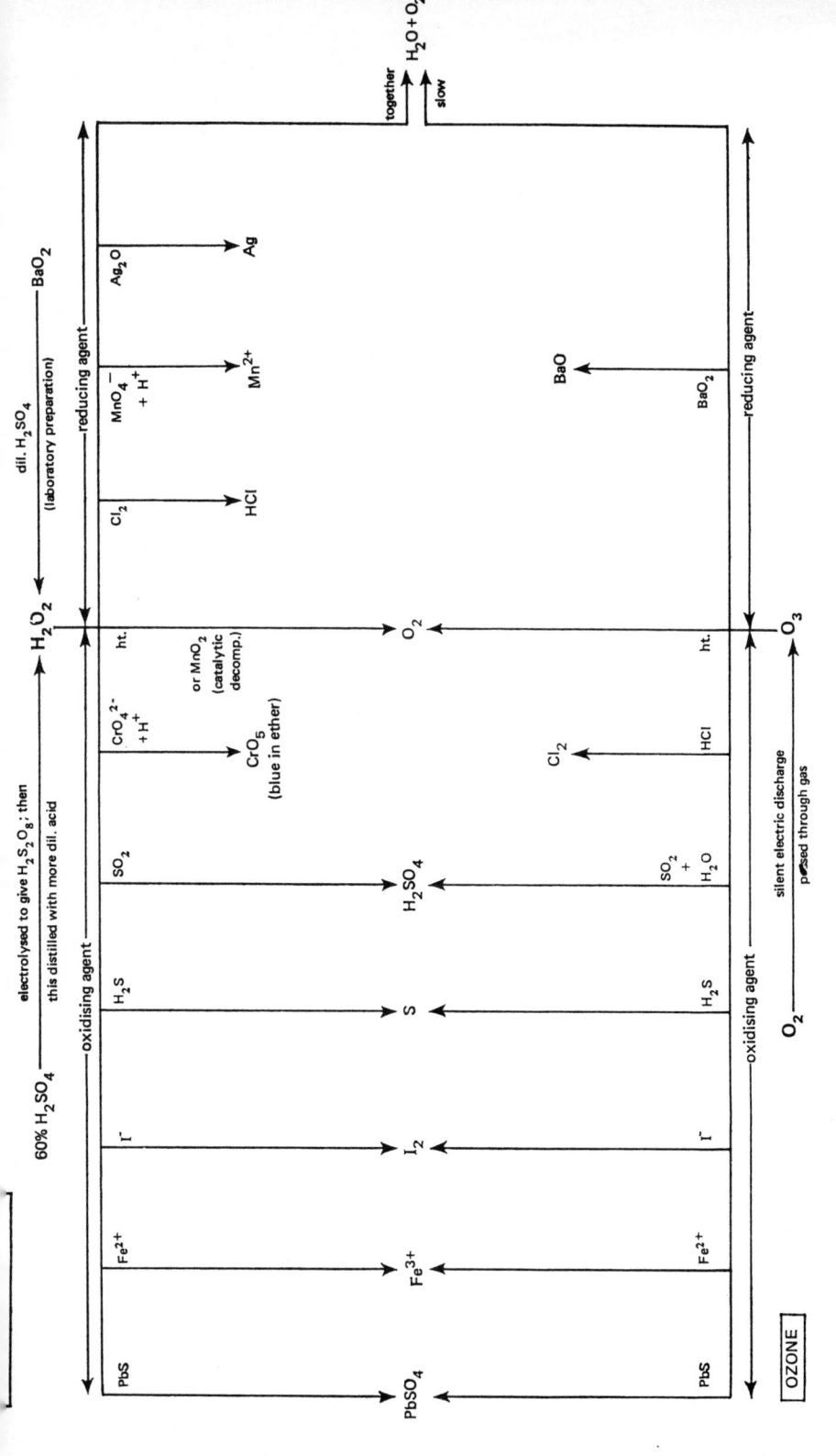

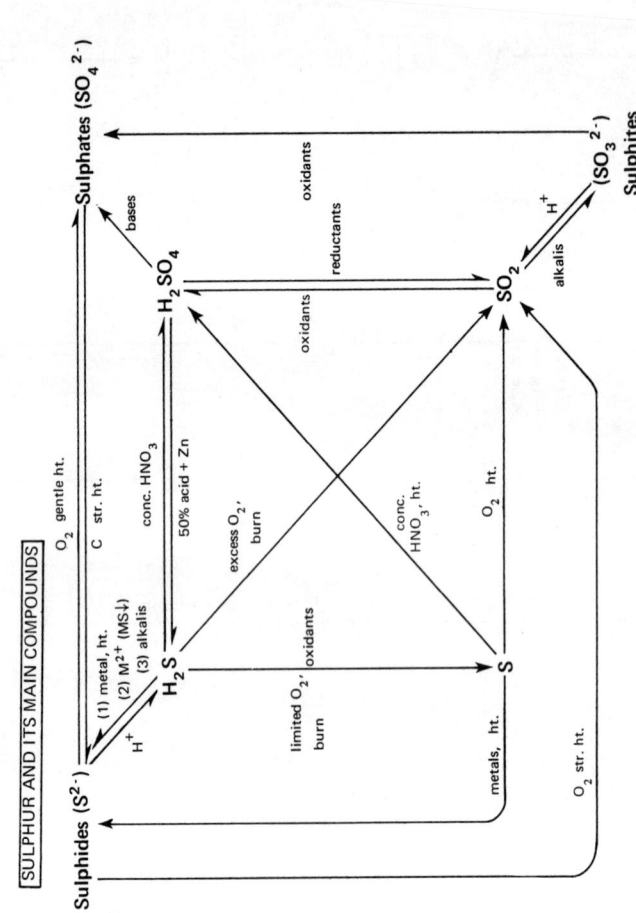

SULPHUR AND ITS MAIN COMPOUNDS

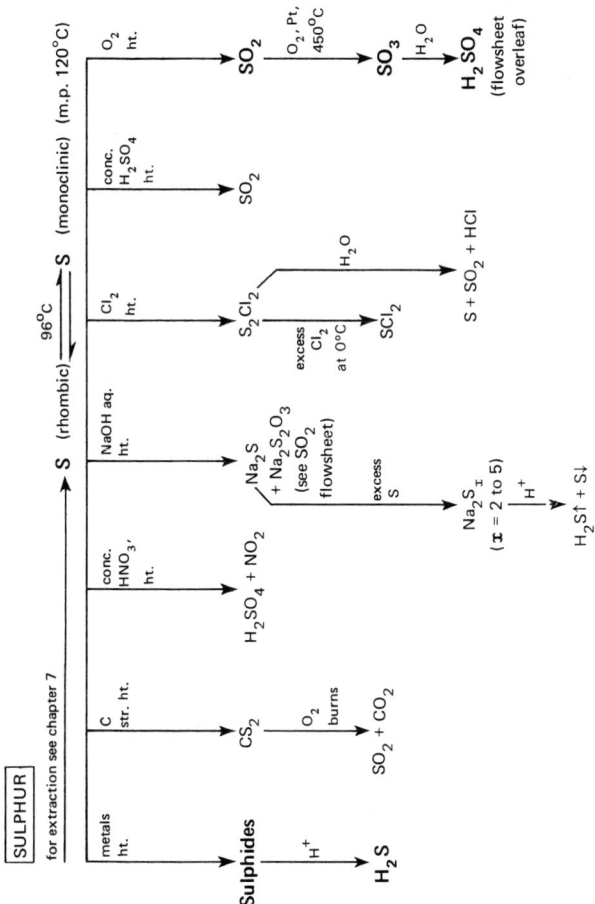

SULPHUR

for extraction see chapter 7

S (rhombic) $\underset{96°C}{\rightleftharpoons}$ S (monoclinic)   (m.p. 120°C)

metals
ht.

C
str. ht.

conc.
HNO_3,
ht.

NaOH aq.
ht.

Cl_2
ht.

conc.
H_2SO_4
ht.

O_2
ht.

Sulphides

CS_2

$H_2SO_4 + NO_2$

Na_2S
$+ Na_2S_2O_3$
(see SO_2
flowsheet)

S_2Cl_2

SO_2

SO_2

H^+

O_2
burns

excess
S

excess
Cl_2
at 0°C

H_2O

O_2, Pt,
450°C

H_2S

$SO_2 + CO_2$

Na_2S_x
($x = 2$ to 5)

SCl_2

$S + SO_2 + HCl$

SO_3

H^+

$H_2S\uparrow + S\downarrow$

H_2O

H_2SO_4
(flowsheet
overleaf)

HYDROGEN SULPHIDE

$$FeS \xrightarrow[\text{(laboratory preparation).}]{\text{dilute HCl}} H_2S$$

aq. ox. agents, e.g. Fe^{3+}, MnO_4^-, 50% HNO_3 → S

Cl_2 → S + HCl

O_2 (limited) burn → S + H_2O

O_2 (excess) burn → (H₂O also formed)

Pb^{2+} (and many others) → PbS↓

most metals, ht. → Sulphides + H_2 ⇌ H^+

$$Na_2S \xleftarrow[H^+]{NaOH} \qquad Na_2S \xrightarrow[\text{NaOH}]{\text{excess } H_2S} NaHS$$

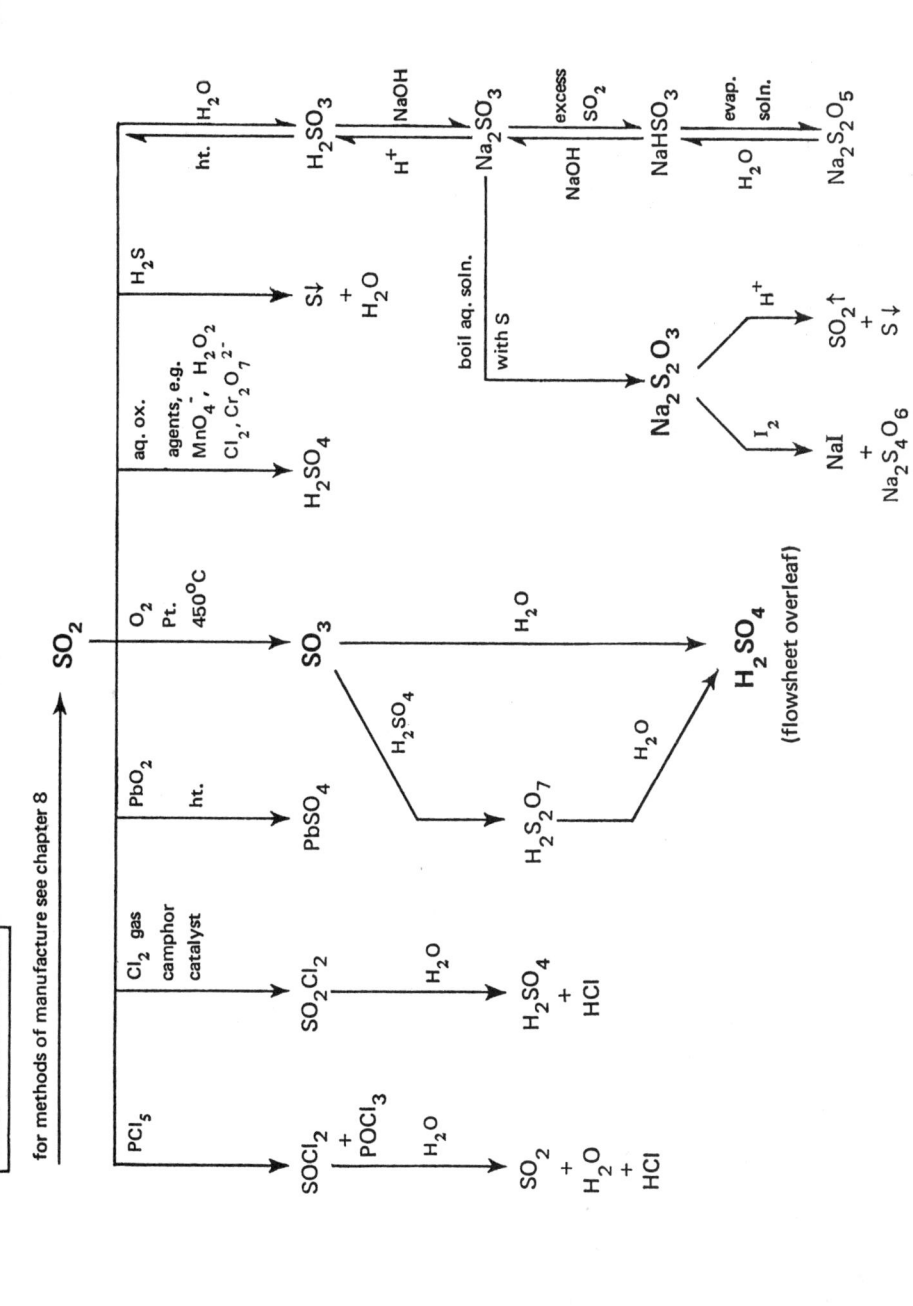

SULPHUR DIOXIDE

for methods of manufacture see chapter 8

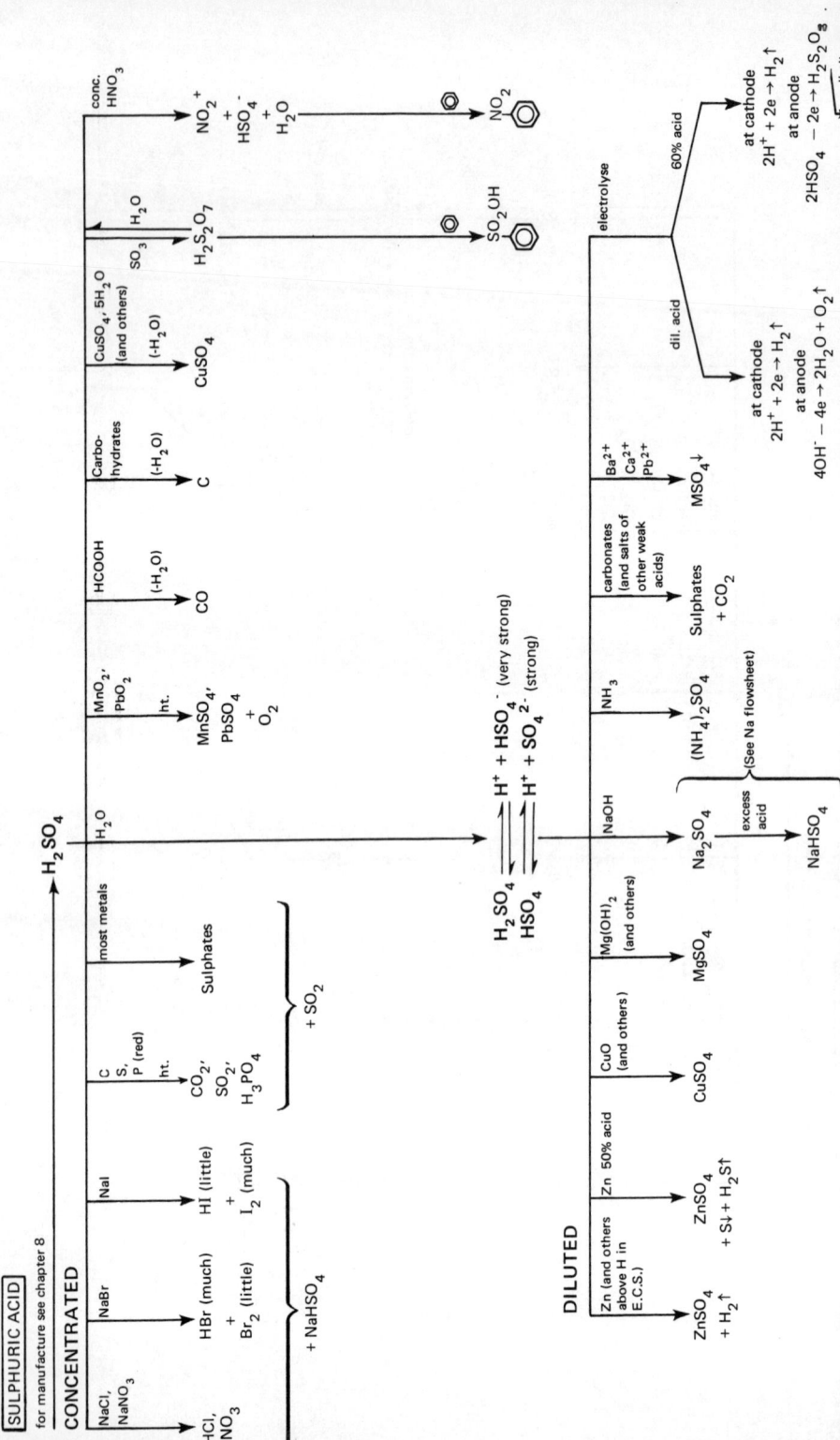

SULPHURIC ACID

for manufacture see chapter 8

S_8 rings predominate just above the m.p. These soon break to give short chain molecules which at higher temperatures (ca. 180°C) join together to give very long chain molecules (sharp rise in viscosity). The long chains break down again as the b.p. (444°C) is approached. If the liquid near the b.p. is cooled rapidly (e.g. by pouring into cold water) the above equilibria are 'frozen' while S_μ chains predominate; the chains are thus retained, producing an elastic form of the element—**plastic sulphur**. This plastic sulphur quickly becomes brittle at room temperature as it reverts to the stable allotrope, rhombic.

Sulphur vapour at the boiling point has a vapour density corresponding with S_8 molecules; at 1000°C dissociation to S_2 is almost complete.

SECTION H

GROUP VII: FLUORINE, CHLORINE, BROMINE and IODINE

	Atomic number	Electronic configuration of atoms
F	9	2, 7
Cl	17	2, 8, 7
Br	35	2, 8, 18, 7
I	53	2, 8, 18, 18, 7

Atoms of these elements (the **halogens**) contain seven electrons in their outer (valency) shells—one fewer than the nearest noble gases.

The halogens are the most electronegative elements in their periods, while fluorine, with the smallest atomic radius, is the most electronegative of all the elements.

These elements need only one electron to form a stable noble

(*Continued on page 78*)

	Fluorine	Chlorine	Bromine	Iodine
Elements General	pale yellow gas	pale yellow-green gas	red-brown liquid; b.p. 59°C red-brown vapour	black, lustrous solid; sublimes, violet vapour
Reaction with water	oxygen evolved $2F_2 + 2H_2O \rightarrow 4HF + O_2$	fairly soluble, pale green soln. $Cl_2 + H_2O \rightleftharpoons HCl + HOCl$ oxygen evolved very slowly	less soluble than Cl_2; much less hydrolysed; brown soln. $Br_2 + H_2O \rightleftharpoons HBr + HOBr$	only very slightly soluble; pale brown soln.; negligible hydrolysis
Reaction with aqueous alkali (NaOH)	dil. soln.—fluorine monoxide $2F_2 + 2OH^- \rightarrow$ $2F^- + F_2O + H_2O$ conc. soln.—oxygen evolved $2F_2 + 4OH^- \rightarrow$ $4F^- + O_2 + 2H_2O$	cold dil. soln.; excess alkali—chloride and hypochlorite $Cl_2 + 2OH^- \rightarrow$ $Cl^- + OCl^- + H_2O$ hot, conc. soln.; excess chlorine—chloride and chlorate $3Cl_2 + 6OH^- \rightarrow$ $5Cl^- + ClO_3^- + 3H_2O$	similar to chlorine	similar to chlorine and bromine except that first reaction is reversible and OI^- changes rapidly to I^- and IO_3^- $3OI^- \rightarrow 2I^- + IO_3^-$
Reaction with hydrogen	explosive, even in dark; HF formed $H_2 + F_2 \rightarrow 2HF$	explosive in sunlight, otherwise H_2 burns smoothly in Cl_2 $H_2 + Cl_2 \rightarrow 2HCl$	reversible; heat required to establish equilibrium quickly $H_2 + Br_2 \rightleftharpoons 2HBr$	reversible, as for bromine $H_2 + I_2 \rightleftharpoons 2HI$
Reaction with non-metals	all react except N and O	all react except C, N and O	all react except C, Si, N, O	only P, As and other halogens react
Oxidising power	very powerful, strongest of all elements	strong	moderate	weak
Reaction with metals, e.g. Fe	most burn burns forming FeF_3	many burn burns forming $FeCl_3$	few burn in vapour forms mixture $FeBr_2$, $FeBr_3$	none burns in vapour forms FeI_2

	Cl, Br, I displaced $F_2 + 2Cl^- \rightarrow 2F^- + Cl_2$	Br, I displaced $Cl_2 + 2Br^- \rightarrow 2Cl^- + Br_2$	only I displaced $Br_2 + 2I^- \rightarrow 2Br^- + I_2$	none displaced
Halogen / halogen displacement				
Hydrides	HF; weak acid (much hydrogen bonding)—also abnormally high b.p. (19·5°C)	HCl; colourless gas; aqueous soln. strongly acidic; oxidised by air only in presence of heated catalyst ($CuCl_2$) $4HCl + O_2 \rightarrow 2Cl_2 + 2H_2O$	HBr; similar to HCl, but oxidised slowly by air on standing—aq. solns. become orange with free Br_2 and Br_3^- $4HBr + O_2 \rightarrow 2Br_2 + 2H_2O$ $Br^- + Br_2 \rightleftharpoons Br_3^-$	HI; similar to HCl, HBr, but far more readily oxidised by air to I_2—aq. solns. become brown owing to production of I_2 and I_3^-
Action of oxidising agents	no effect on HF	only most powerful (MnO_2, $KMnO_4$ etc.) oxidise HCl to Cl_2	HBr oxidised by even moderately powerful reagents	HI oxidised by all oxidising agents. It is a very powerful reducing agent
Metal halides Solubility in water	generally insoluble, but fluorides of following are exceptions: K, Na, NH_4^+, Ag, Hg(II)	chlorides generally soluble; exceptions: AgCl, Hg_2Cl_2, CuCl, $PbCl_2$ (appreciably soluble in hot water)	similar to chlorides	similar to chlorides and bromides but, in addition, HgI_2 also insoluble
Silver halides	AgF, water soluble	AgCl, white, insol. in water, easily sol. in ammonia $Ag^+ + 2NH_3 \rightleftharpoons Ag(NH_3)_2^+$	AgBr, pale cream, insoluble in water, soluble in ammonia only with great difficulty	AgI, cream, insoluble in water and ammonia
Oxyacids	none formed	four: HOCl, $HClO_2$, $HClO_3$, $HClO_4$	two: HOBr, $HBrO_3$	HOI, HIO_3, HIO_4 and several other periodic acids

gas configuration. Thus the principal valency is one. This may
be

(a) *electrovalent*, when uninegative ions are formed

$$X + e \longrightarrow X^-$$

and this occurs in reactions with nearly all metals;

(b) *covalent*, as in HCl, CCl_4, PBr_3, etc;—in compounds
formed with other non-metals.

Apart from fluorine (like O and N, the first members of the
two preceding groups) the halogens can also show higher
valencies, including the group valency of 7, e.g. $HBrO_3$, $HClO_4$,
Cl_2O_7.

The changes as the group is descended (and atomic radius
increases) may be summarised:

(i) Electronegativity, and therefore reactivity, decreases
since there is a decreasing tendency for the outer shells to capture an electron the further they are from the positive nucleus.

(ii) The oxidising power of the free halogen decreases sharply
as the tendency to capture electrons decreases.

$$F \longrightarrow Cl \longrightarrow Br \longrightarrow I$$

powerful			feeble
oxidising			oxidising
agent			agent

(iii) Fluorine raises the combined state of an element to its
highest covalence, e.g. sulphur (6) in SF_6, iodine (7) in IF_7.

(iv) Hydrogen fluoride exhibits considerable hydrogen bonding, HCl very little, and HBr and HI none. Thus HF has an
extremely anomalous b.p. (HF, $19.5°C$; HCl, $-84°C$)—as has
water. HF is also a very much weaker acid than HCl, HBr, HI,
which dissociate almost completely in water

$$HCl + H_2O \rightleftharpoons H_3O^+ + Cl^-$$

CHEMICAL PROPERTIES

These are summarised and compared in the table on p. 76.

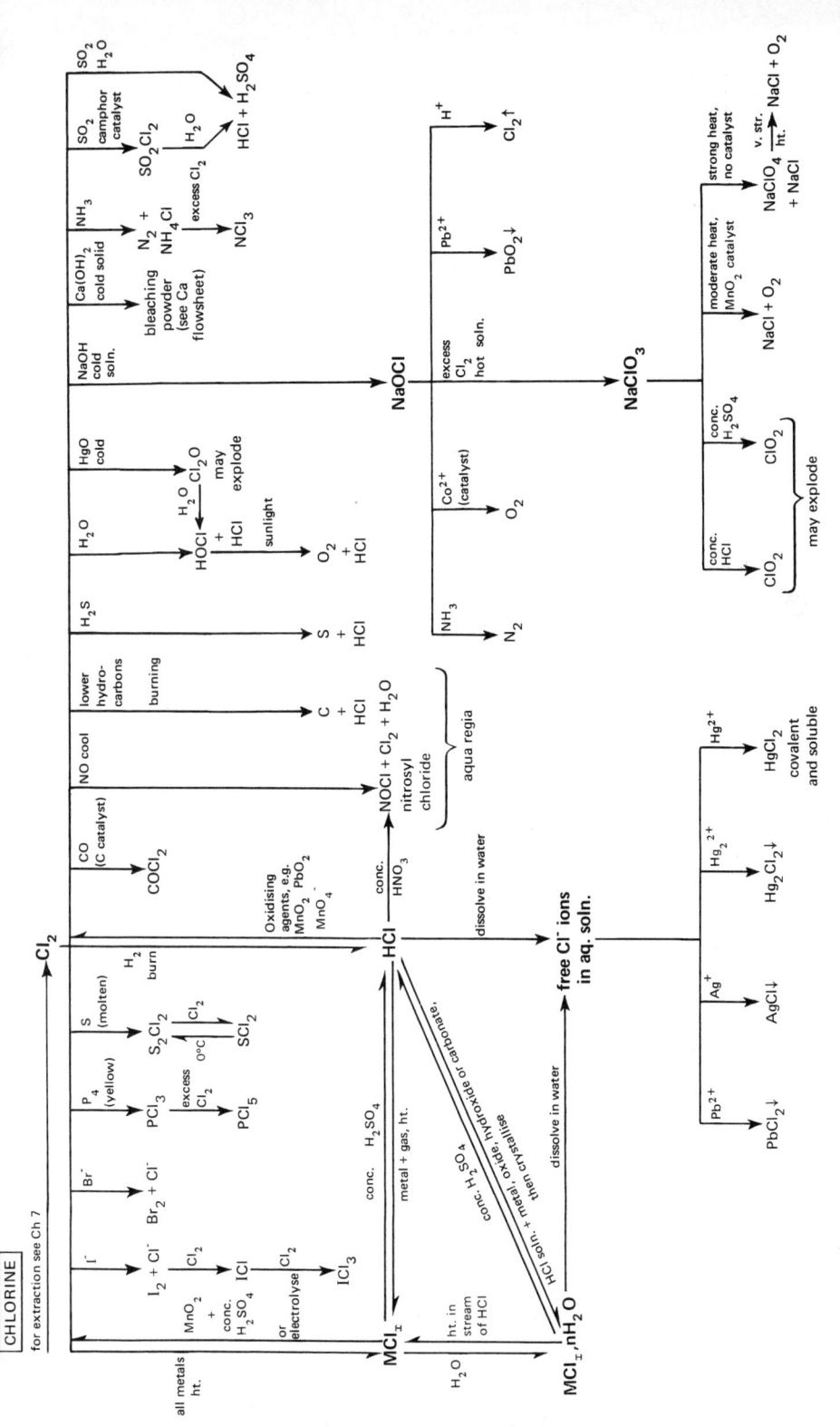

CHLORINE

for extraction see Ch 7

80

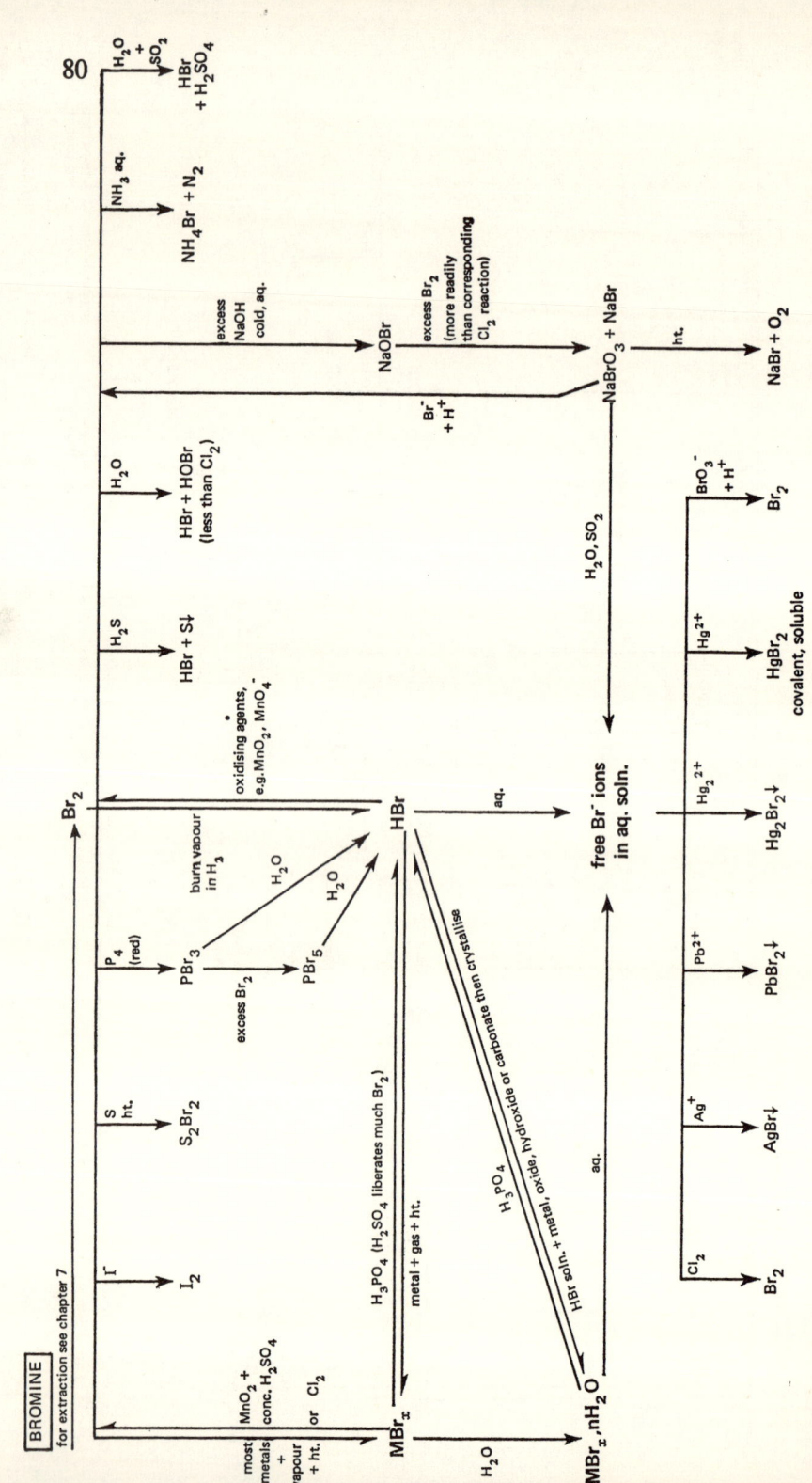

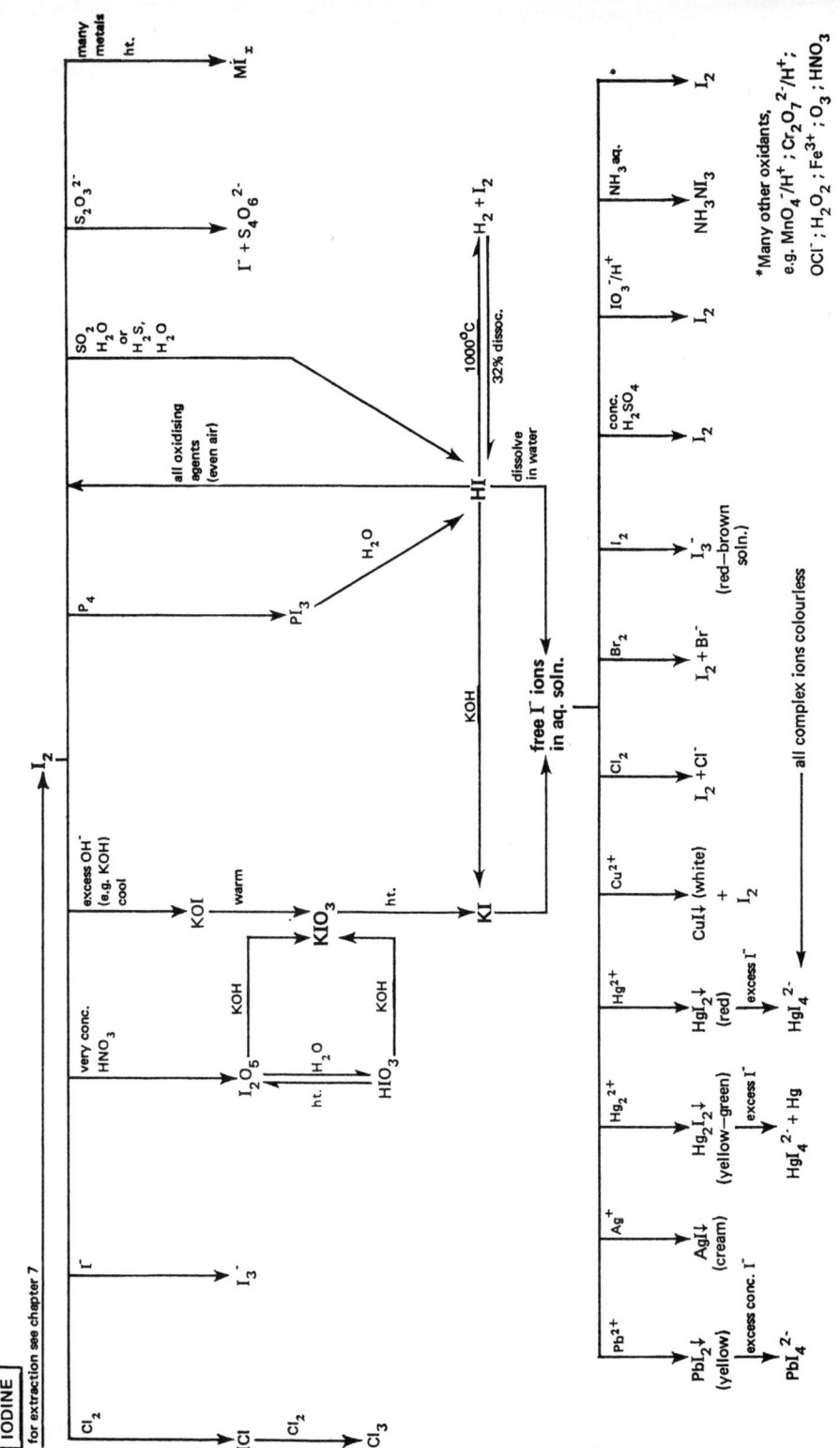

IODINE

for extraction see chapter 7

Chapter 5

The Noble Gases

	Atomic number	Electronic configuration of atoms
He	2	2
Ne	10	2, 8
Ar	18	2, 8, 8
Kr	36	2, 8, 18, 8
Xe	54	2, 8, 18, 18, 8
Rn	86	2, 8, 18, 32, 18, 8

ELECTRONIC STRUCTURE

All have outer (valency) shells containing eight electrons (except He which has a maximum capacity of two electrons in its outer shell) and these 'octets' are very stable configurations —accounting for the almost complete unreactivity of these elements.

DISCOVERY AND ISOLATION

All are found in air except radon, which is radioactive (half-life $^{222}_{86}Rn = 3.8$ days). Argon is abundant ($\simeq$ 30 times as much as carbon dioxide in air) but the others are present in very small quantities.

They were discovered by Cavendish (1785) who sparked atmospheric nitrogen with oxygen and, after removal of the NO_2 produced, found that about 1% of the original 'nitrogen' volume remained. This received little further attention until Rayleigh (1892) found that atmospheric nitrogen was slightly denser than nitrogen prepared from ammonia. He confirmed Cavendish's results and showed that the 'residual' gas gave a different spectrum from that of nitrogen. Ramsay (1894) also isolated a gas from air by passing atmospheric nitrogen backwards and forwards over hot magnesium (removing N_2 as Mg_3N_2); the gas produced was found to be inert and was called argon (though it was subsequently found to be a mixture).

Helium was discovered following the observation that certain uranium ores evolved an unreactive gas when heated with acids. Further investigation indicated that this was (a) a new element whose spectrum was identical with lines observed in the sun's chromosphere and (b) not a product of a reaction between the acid and the mineral but a gaseous radioactive decay product (α particles) that had been occluded by the mineral and merely physically released on heating.

The discovery of two 'noble' gases and speculation that they were members of a new group of the Periodic Table led to search for other, similar, elements. Success resulted from the fractional distillation of the residual gas 'argon' when neon, krypton and xenon were isolated. Radon—a radioactive disintegration product of radium—was discovered in 1904.

$$^{226}_{88}Ra \longrightarrow\ ^{222}_{86}Rn +\ ^{4}_{2}He$$

The principal source of helium is now natural gas (often 1% He) obtained from petroleum wells. The helium (which has the lowest of all known b.ps.) is obtained by extreme cooling, when the other (mainly hydrocarbon) constituents condense.

Other noble gases are obtained by the fractional distillation of liquid air.

NOBLE GAS COMPOUNDS

The likelihood of atoms of noble gases entering into chemical combination increases with atomic radius He → Kr as the octet is influenced less by the nucleus.

No compounds involving He, Ne and Ar have been produced (other than 'clathrate compounds'—in which the noble gas atoms are trapped in the lattices of solid compounds, e.g. ice).

In 1962 the first compound of xenon was produced by the interaction of Xe and PtF_6. The red crystalline product was of formula $Xe(PtF_6)_x$ where x lies between 1 and 2. Many other compounds of xenon (all involving the highly electronegative elements F and O) have since been prepared, e.g.

XeF_2	colourless, cryst., m.p. 140°C, stable
XeF_4	colourless, cryst., m.p. 114°C, stable
$XeOF_4$	colourless, liquid, m.p. −28°C, stable
XeO_3	colourless, cryst., explosive
Cs_2XeF_8	colourless, cryst., stable to 400°C.

In 1965, KrF_2 was prepared by passing a discharge through a mixture of the gases. The existence of a fluoride of radon has been established, but the rapid radioactive decay of radon and the energy liberated make assessment difficult.

Chapter 6

The Transition Elements

Sc		Ti	V	Cr	Mn	Fe	Co	Ni	Cu	Zn
Y		Zr	Nb	Mo	Tc	Ru	Rh	Pd	Ag	Cd
La		* Hf	Ta	W	Re	Os	Ir	Pt	Au	Hg
Ac	*									

14 elements inserted here (the lanthanides)
at. nos. 58–71
└─ 14 elements inserted here (the actinides)
at nos. 90–92 natural, 93→ artificial

DEFINITION

No short, simple definition is completely satisfactory. The following, however, is frequently encountered:

A **transition element** is one in which an inner shell is in the process of being filled.

An inspection of the table of electronic configurations facing p. 1 indicates that in passing from scandium (at. no. 21) through eight elements to zinc (at. no. 30) the number of electrons in the outer shell remains constant at 2 (except for Cu and Cr) while the penultimate shell is expanded beyond the stable octet of calcium to 18. These elements (Sc → Zn) are transition elements. There are other transition series in the periods 4, 5, 6 and 7.

More than two-thirds of all the elements are transition elements.

TYPES OF TRANSITION ELEMENTS

There are two types:

(*a*) **Outer transition elements**—in which the outer but one

85

shell is being filled. There are 10 of these in each of periods 4, 5 and 6. Actinium (at. no. 89) is the first member of a probable fourth series in period 7.

(b) **Inner transition elements**—in which the outer but two shell is being filled. These are the *lanthanides* or *rare earth* elements, 14 of which occur in the sixth period while the antepenultimate shell is expanding from 18 to 32 electrons. These elements are chemically very similar since all have similar configurations in the outer shells, viz. 9 and 2 (or 8 and 2). A second inner transition series (the *actinides*) starts with thorium in the seventh period and extends into the artificially made transuranic elements.

CHARACTERISTICS OF THE TRANSITION ELEMENTS

1. All are lustrous metals, white in colour (except Cu and Au), of high density and (except Zn, Cd, Hg) of high m.p.—i.e. they have the physical characteristics which are usually considered to be typically metallic.

2. The atomic radii of the transition elements are all of the same order.

3. They readily form alloys with one another and with some non-transition metals such as tin and lead. This is attributable to the similar atomic radii—permitting the interchange of ions in the crystal lattices without causing undue distortion.

4. All are metals capable of forming positive ions, though none is as highly electropositive as the metals of Groups I and II. Many (e.g. Mn, Fe, Zn) are capable of displacing hydrogen from aqueous solutions of strong, non-oxidising acids such as HCl, while several occur below hydrogen in the E.C.S. (e.g. Cu, Hg, Ag).

As a transition metal group is descended the metals become **less** electropositive (i.e. the reverse of the trend observed in Groups I, II, etc. of the non-transition elements). This is because the increasing positive charge on the nucleus exerts greater attraction for the outer electrons, since there is little change in atomic radius.

5. Most of these elements exhibit highly variable valency, e.g. in the first series the valencies shown are

Sc	Ti	V	Cr	Mn	Fe	Co	Ni	Cu	Zn
3	2, 3, 4	2, 3, 4, 5	2, 3, 4, 6	2, 3, 4, 6, 7	2, 3			1, 2	2

It is noteworthy that the majority have the common valency 2 —as might be expected from the outer shell configuration.

The lower valencies are usually ionic, positive ions being formed by the loss of 1, 2 or 3 electrons, e.g.

Fe	2, 8, 14, 2	Cu	2, 8, 18, 1
Fe^{2+}	2, 8, 14	Cu^+	2, 8, 18
Fe^{3+}	2, 8, 13	Cu^{2+}	2, 8, 17

while the higher valencies tend to be covalencies, e.g. in the chromate(VI), CrO_4^{2-}, and manganate (VII), permanganate), MnO_4^-, ions, the metals in these higher valency compounds showing similarities to the non-metals.

acidic oxides:

$$CrO_3 \text{ (cf. } SO_3) \qquad Mn_2O_7 \text{ (cf. } Cl_2O_7)$$

oxyacids and salts:

$$H_2CrO_4 \text{ (cf. } H_2SO_4) \qquad KMnO_4 \text{ (cf. } KClO_4)$$

6. Because of their similar outer electronic configurations transition metals show considerable similarities to their neighbours in the same period as well as in the same group.

7. They readily participate in complex ion formation, e.g.

$$Fe(CN)_6^{3-}, \quad Cu(NH_3)_4^{2+}, \quad Ag(NH_3)_2^+, \quad HgI_4^{2-}$$

and this is an important feature of the chemistry of the transition metals.

8. The majority form coloured ions, e.g. $Cr(H_2O)_6^{3+}$—green, $Cu(H_2O)_4^{2+}$—blue, $Fe(H_2O)_6^{3+}$—brown, whereas the ions of

the non-transition elements are colourless. The colour of transition metal compounds is associated with electron movements in an incomplete inner shell; when this shell becomes full the ions are colourless, e.g. Cu^+ (2, 8, 18), Zn^{2+} (2, 8, 18).

9. Transition elements often show considerable catalytic activity, largely due to their ability to adsorb molecules from the gas phase. Examples of this type of heterogeneous catalysis are Fe in the Haber process, Pt or V_2O_5 in the contact process, Ni in the hydrogenation of oils and fats. Variable valency also promotes their catalytic power by permitting the formation of a wider range of intermediate compounds, e.g. $MnO_2/KClO_3$ (see p. 135 of *Revision Notes for Advanced Level Physical Chemistry*).

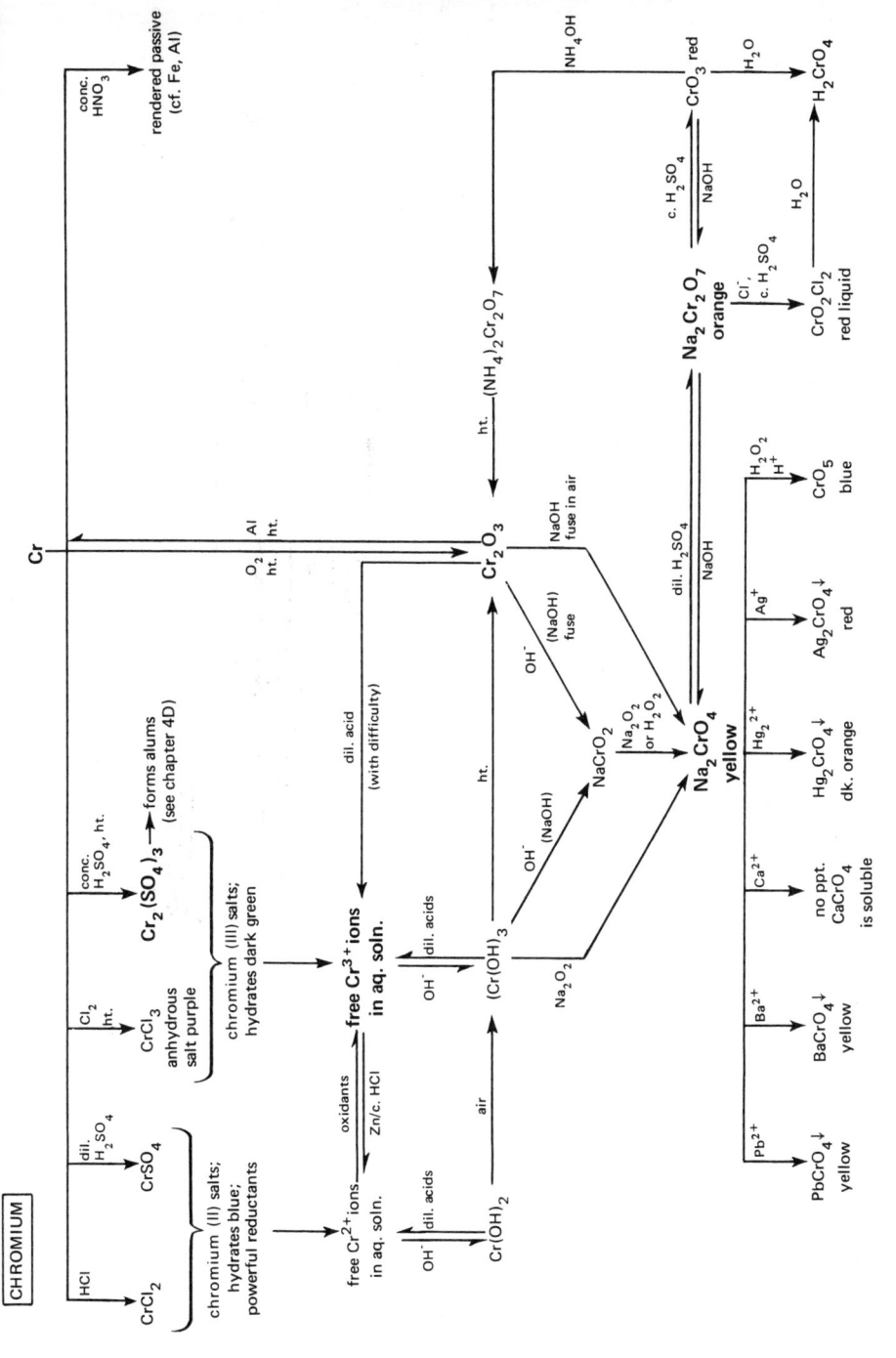

CHROMIUM

MANGANESE

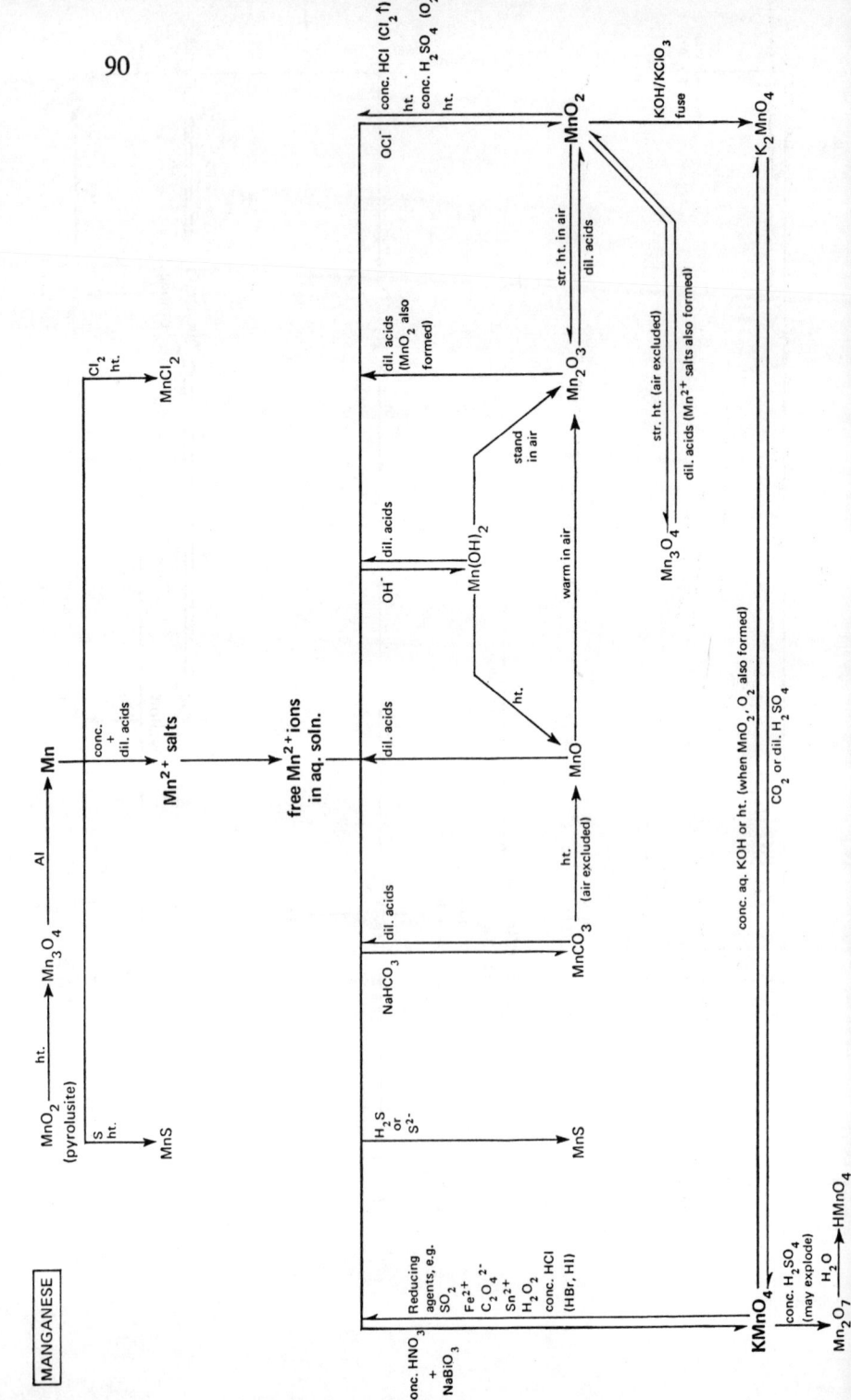

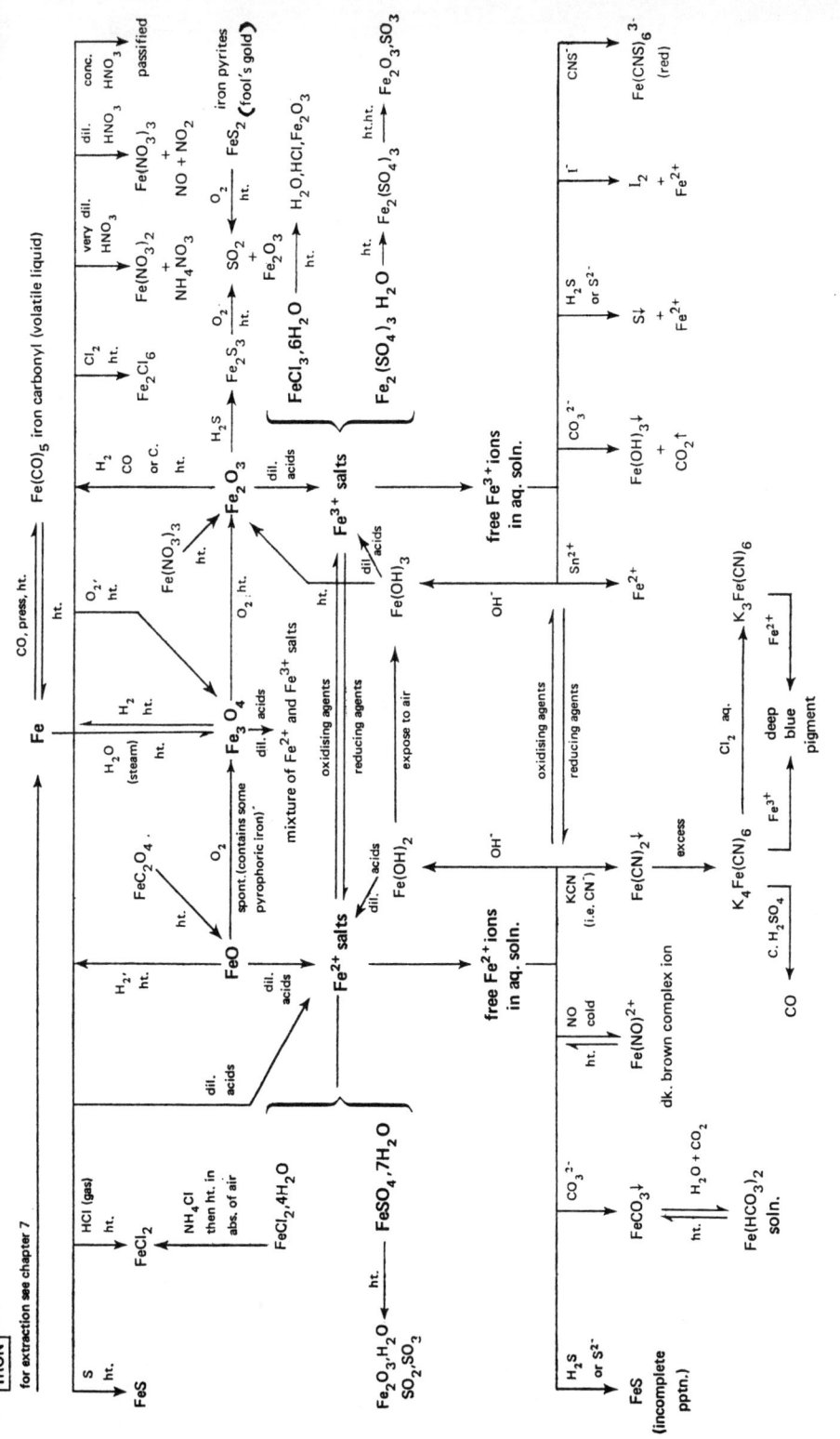

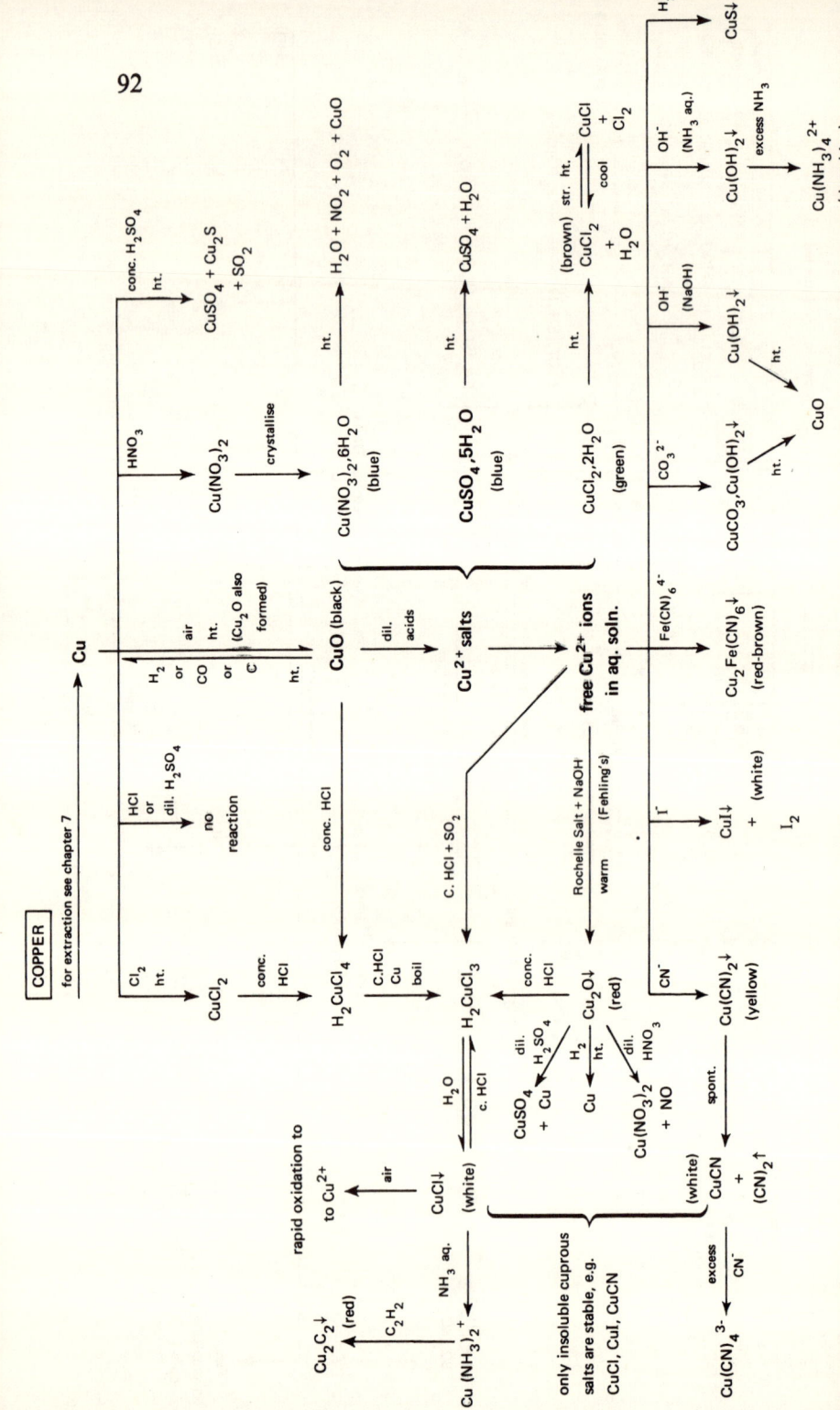

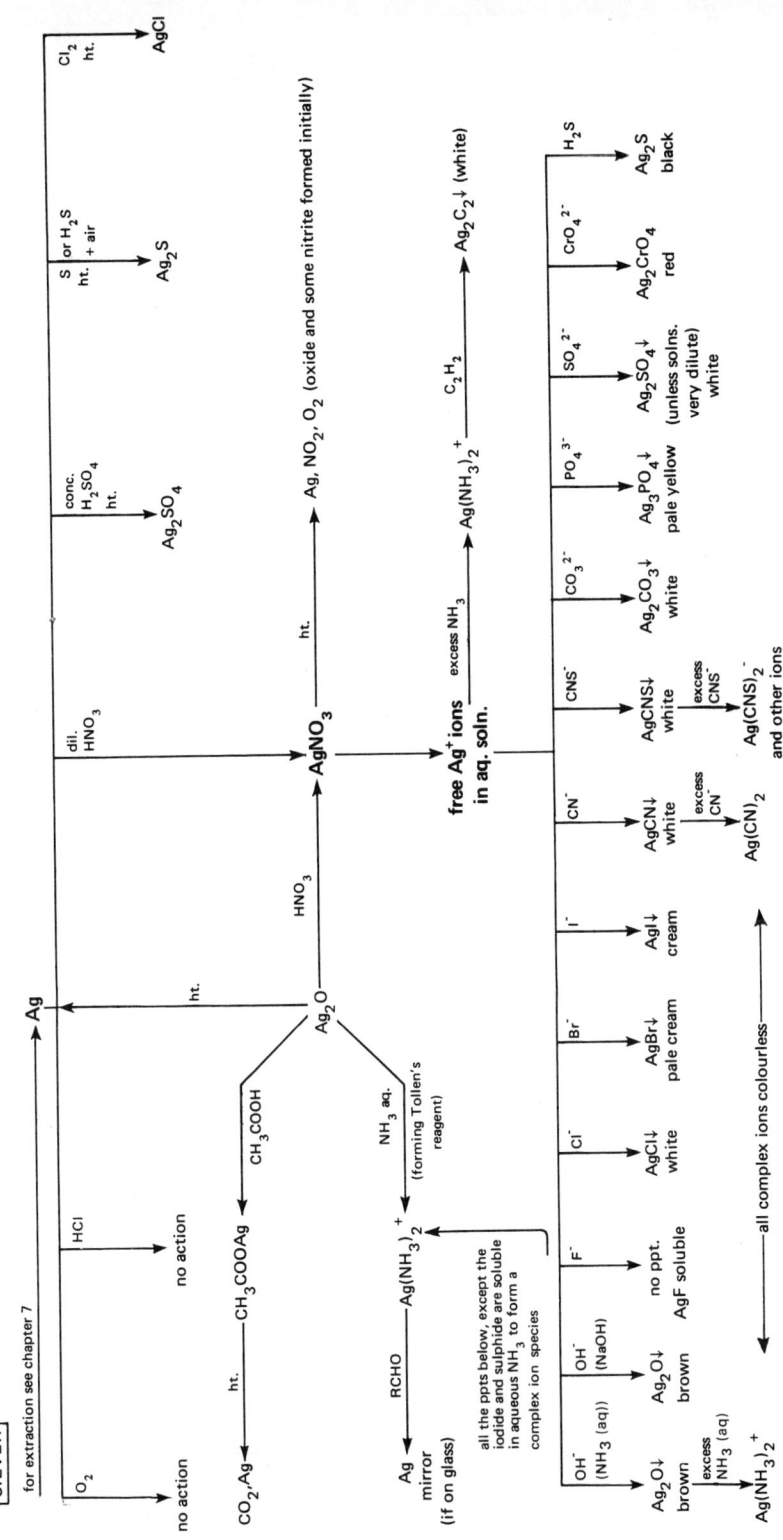

SILVER

for extraction see chapter 7

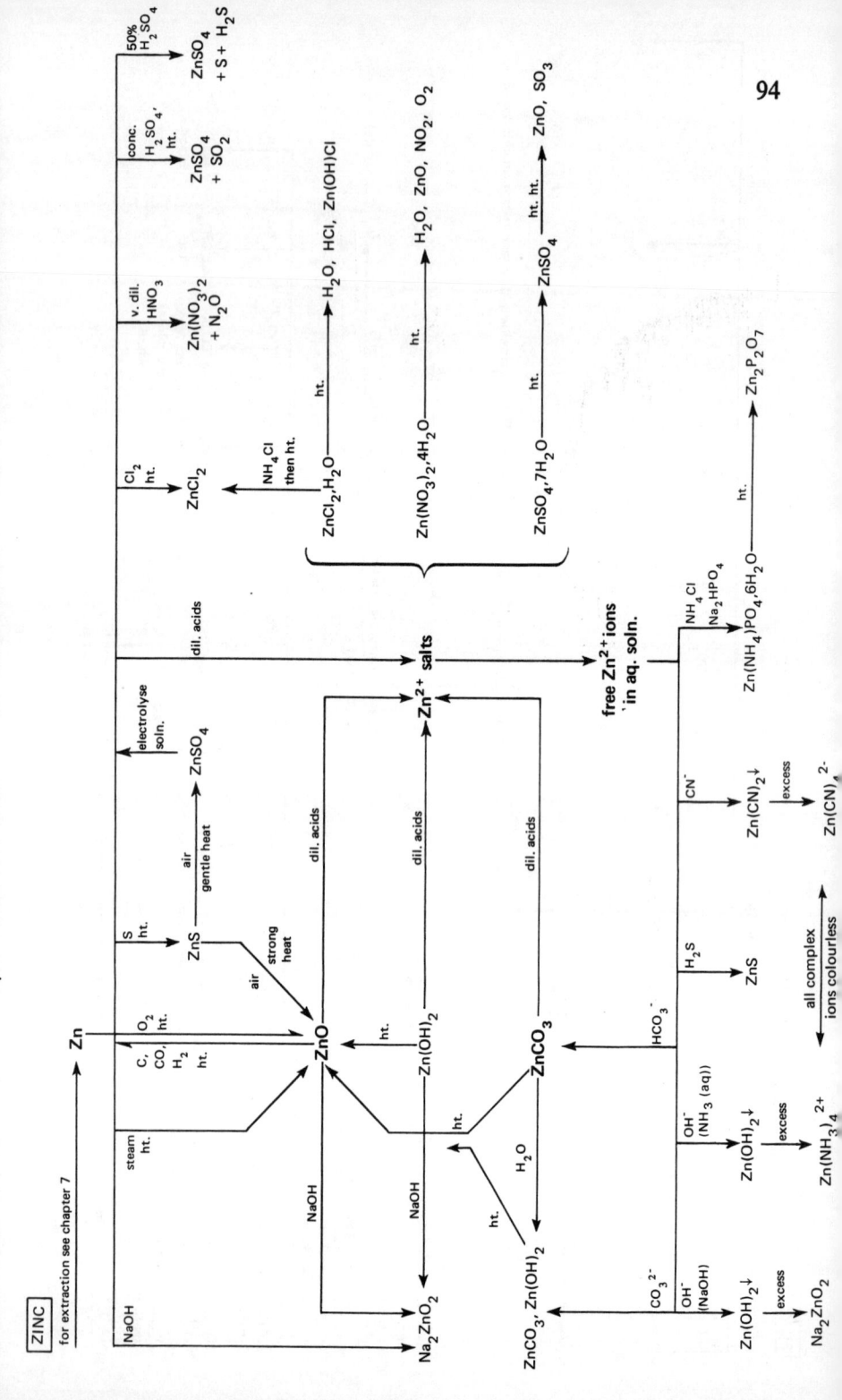

94

MERCURY

for extraction see chapter 7

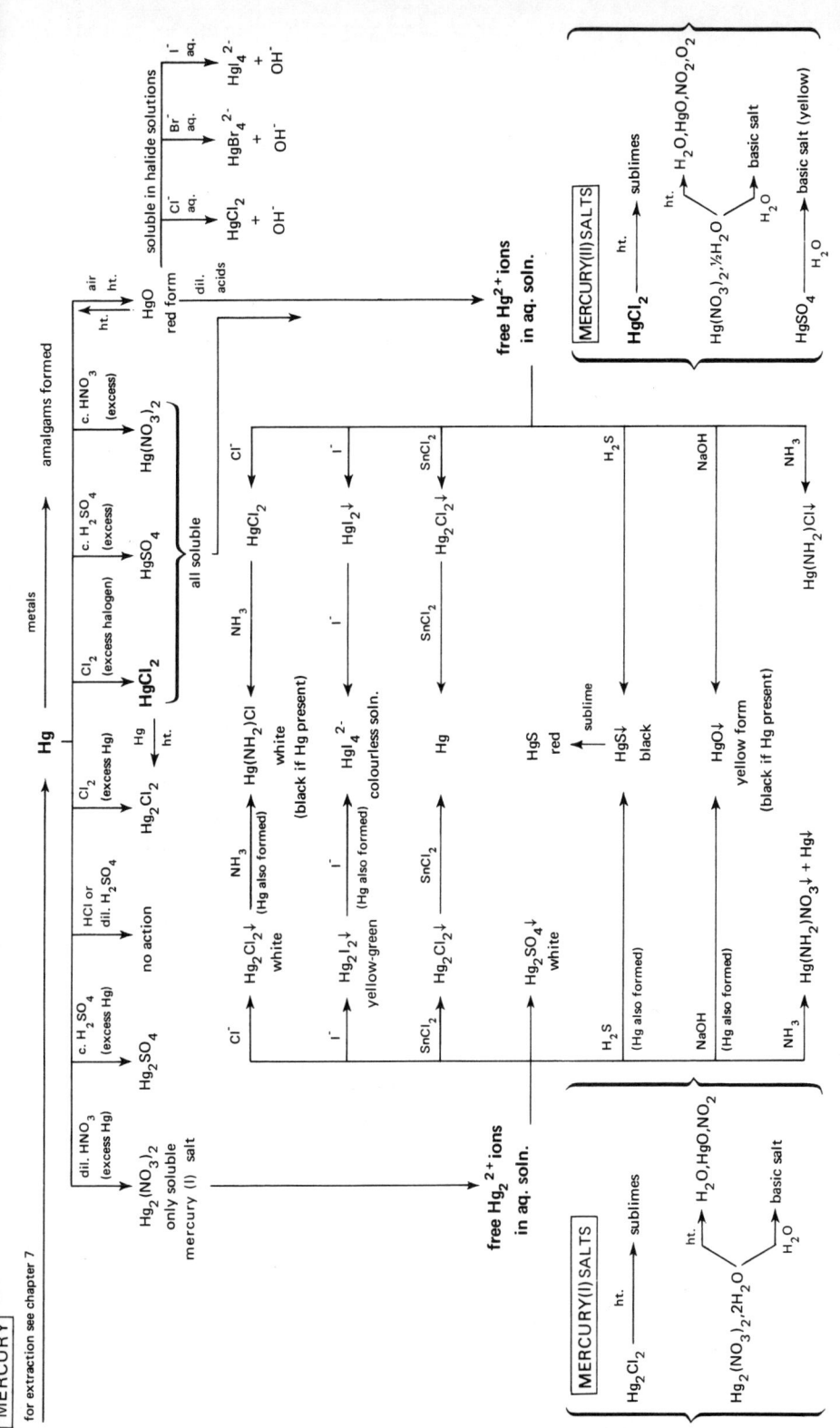

The Extraction of Elements

SECTION A: THE METALS

The isolation of a metal from one of its compounds is essentially a process of reduction

$$M^{n+} + ne \longrightarrow M$$

and the ease with which this is effected depends primarily on the electropositivity of the metal concerned, i.e. on its position in the electrochemical series. For example, a highly electropositive metal is one which readily discards electrons to form positive ions and, predictably, the reverse process is very difficult.

In the electrochemical series the metals are arranged in decreasing order of electropositive character, and thus less powerful reducing methods are required for metal extraction as the series is descended. This is illustrated below.

THE ELECTROCHEMICAL SERIES (this includes only a selection of the common metals)

K Ca Na Mg Al Zn Fe Ni Sn Pb Cu Hg Ag

EXTRACTION METHODS

(1) K → Zn, by electrolysis (cathodic reduction)

This is used for the most electropositive metals; reduction occurs at the cathode by electron donation to the positive ions, e.g.

$$K^+ + e \longrightarrow K$$

The electrolyte (usually the chloride) must be fused, since aqueous solutions contain hydrogen ions which would be discharged in preference to the metal ion. K, Ca, Na, Mg, Al and Zn are all extracted by electrolysis.

(2) Zn → Sn, by an external reducing agent

The reducing agent usually employed is carbon (e.g. coke) on account of its cheapness, but others are used. The following table indicates the agents employed in the reduction of ores of some metals of moderate electropositivity

Metal	Compound reduced	Reducing agent
Zn	ZnO	C
Fe	Fe_2O_3; Fe_3O_4	CO (from C)
Ni	NiO	H_2
Sn	SnO_2	C
Mn	Mn_3O_4	Al
Cr	Cr_2O_3	Al
Ti	$TiCl_4$	Na

Mg, though highly electropositive, is now produced in fairly large quantities by the reduction of MgO with Si (contained in an Fe/Si alloy, ferrosilicon).

(3) Pb and Cu, by auto-reduction

In this type of process no external reducing agent is used. The metal sulphide is partially converted to the oxide by roasting in air, and then the oxide–sulphide mixture is heated strongly in the absence of air:

$$2PbS + 3O_2 \longrightarrow 2PbO + 2SO_2$$
then
$$PbS + 2PbO \longrightarrow 3Pb + SO_2$$

(4) Hg and below

These metals frequently occur native. Extraction from the ores is usually effected by an external reducing agent but the reduction is always easy, e.g. silver is produced by displacement with zinc

$$2[Ag(CN)_2]^- + Zn \longrightarrow [Zn(CN)_4]^{2-} + 2Ag$$

SODIUM

Source: rock salt (NaCl)

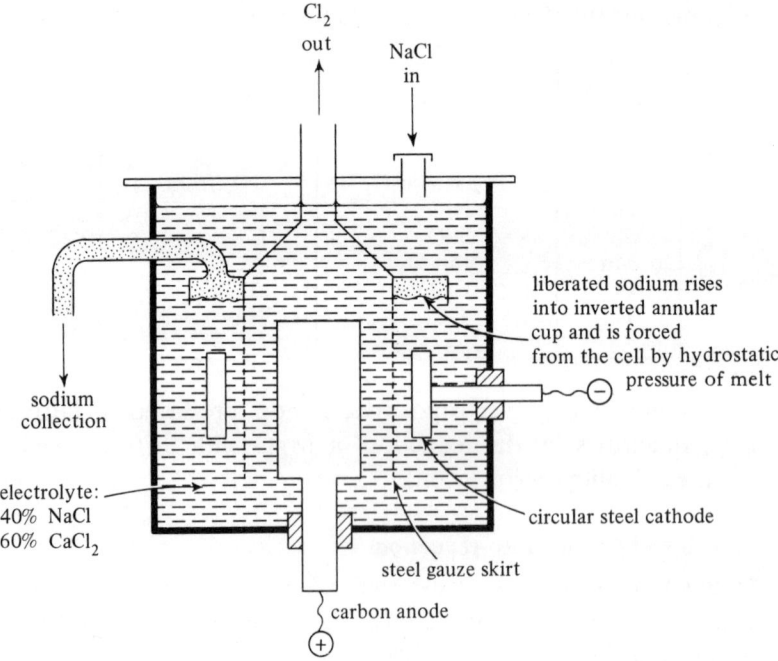

Calcium chloride is added to the sodium chloride to lower its m.p. from 800°C to 600°C. If this were not done (*a*) much sodium (b.p. 880°C) would vaporise, and this vapour would ignite in air, (*b*) the liquid sodium and the chlorine would seriously attack the cell materials.

Reaction at cathode:

$$Na^+ + e \longrightarrow Na$$

Ca^{2+} ions are not discharged because Ca has a higher electrode potential than Na (see pp. 9 and 10).

Reaction at anode:

$$Cl^- - e \longrightarrow Cl; \qquad Cl + Cl \longrightarrow Cl_2$$

The molten sodium and chlorine gas rise through the electrolyte and are collected as indicated.

MAGNESIUM

Sources: dolomite $(MgCO_3,CaCO_3)$, magnesite $(MgCO_3)$, carnallite $(KCl,MgCl_2,6H_2O)$, sea water $(0.3\%$ magnesium as $Mg^{2+})$

(1) **The thermal method**

Dolomite is heated strongly:

$$MgCO_3,CaCO_3 \longrightarrow MgO,CaO + 2CO_2$$

and then mixed with ferrosilicon (an Fe/Si alloy) and heated to approx. 1100°C in evacuated steel tubes:

$$2[MgO,CaO] + Si \rightleftharpoons CaSiO_3 + CaO + 2Mg$$

The magnesium vaporises and then condenses at the cooler ends of the steel tubes while the other components are of course involatile. In this way Mg is removed from the equilibrium mixture and the reduction proceeds almost to completion. The cool ends of the reaction tubes are detachable.

(2) **The electrolytic method**

(*a*) *Production of anhydrous magnesium chloride*

    (i) from magnesite—this is strongly heated to give magnesium oxide

$$MgCO_3 \longrightarrow MgO + CO_2$$

and this is mixed with coal, pelleted, and heated in chlorine

$$MgO + C + Cl_2 \longrightarrow MgCl_2 + CO$$

the molten $MgCl_2$ is then electrolysed (see (b) below).

(ii) from sea water—lime is added which precipitates magnesium hydroxide

$$Mg^{2+} + 2OH^- \longrightarrow Mg(OH)_2 \downarrow$$

This is filtered off, calcined to give the oxide

$$Mg(OH)_2 \longrightarrow MgO + H_2O$$

and then converted to anhydrous chloride as in (i) above.

(b) *Electrolysis of the fused chloride*
   Reaction at iron cathode:

$$Mg^{2+} + 2e \longrightarrow Mg$$

   Reaction at carbon anode:

$$Cl^- - e \longrightarrow Cl; \quad Cl + Cl \longrightarrow Cl_2$$

The molten magnesium rises through the molten electrolyte (as also does the chlorine gas, in a shielded anode compartment) and collects on the surface where it is protected from reaction with the air by a stream of unreactive gas.

ALUMINIUM

Sources: bauxite (mainly hydrated alumina $Al_2O_3xH_2O$ with impurities of Fe_2O_3 and SiO_2); cryolite (Na_3AlF_6) a scarce mineral much of which is now produced synthetically.

(a) **The purification of bauxite**
Powdered bauxite is heated under pressure with concentrated caustic soda solution; the alumina and silica dissolve

$$Al_2O_3 + 2OH^- \longrightarrow 2AlO_2^- + H_2O \qquad (1)$$
$$SiO_2 + 2OH^- \longrightarrow SiO_3^{2-} + H_2O$$

while iron(III) oxide and other impurities are insoluble and are removed by filtration.

The aluminate solution is cooled and agitated with seed crystals of alumina; this reverses reaction (1) and hydrated alumina ($Al_2O_3,3H_2O$) is precipitated. The alkaline solution is re-used for a fresh extraction and the hydrated alumina is ignited to obtain anhydrous alumina

$$Al_2O_3,3H_2O \longrightarrow Al_2O_3 + 3H_2O$$

(b) Electrolytic reduction

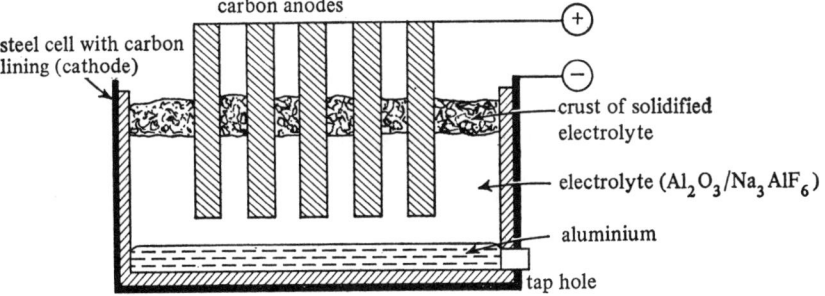

The electrolyte is molten cryolite containing up to 5% of alumina together with some added calcium fluoride to lower the m.p. further.

The alumina ionises in the cryolite:

$$Al_2O_3 \rightleftharpoons Al^{3+} + AlO_3^{3-}$$

Reaction at cathode:

$$Al^{3+} + 3e \longrightarrow Al$$

Reaction at anode:

$$4AlO_3^{3-} - 12e \longrightarrow 2Al_2O_3 + 3O_2$$

The electrolyte is replenished with alumina from time to time, the cryolite not being consumed.

Oxygen liberated at the carbon anodes attacks these to form CO_2 and some CO; the anodes are frequently replaced.

IRON

Sources: haematite, Fe_2O_3; magnetite Fe_3O_4; spathic iron ore $FeCO_3$.

Preparation of ore: The ore is heated to drive off moisture and, in the case of spathic ore, to convert this to iron(III) oxide

$$4FeCO_3 + O_2 \longrightarrow 2Fe_2O_3 + 4CO_2$$

Reduction of ore in the blast furnace

The charge is iron oxide, coke and limestone. Blasts of hot, dry air are injected at the bottom of the furnace through tubes called 'tuyères' and, in the vicinity of these, carbon monoxide (the principal reducing agent) is formed

$$C + O_2 \longrightarrow CO_2; \quad CO_2 + C \longrightarrow 2CO$$

This rises through the charge and, in the top half of the furnace, reduces most of the oxide to solid iron

$$Fe_2O_3 + 3CO \longrightarrow 2Fe + 3CO_2$$

As the charge descends and becomes hotter reduction of un-changed oxide is completed by carbon

$$Fe_2O_3 + 3C \longrightarrow 2Fe + 3CO$$

The descending iron absorbs carbon and its m.p. falls, the metal eventually liquefying and collecting in the hearth.

The limestone in the charge dissociates near the top of the furnace and the quicklime reacts with earthy materials from the ore to give a fusible slag of calcium silicate and calcium aluminate

$$CaCO_3 \rightleftharpoons CaO + CO_2$$

$$CaO + SiO_2 \longrightarrow CaSiO_3; \quad 2CaO + Al_2O_3 \longrightarrow 2Ca(AlO_2)_2$$

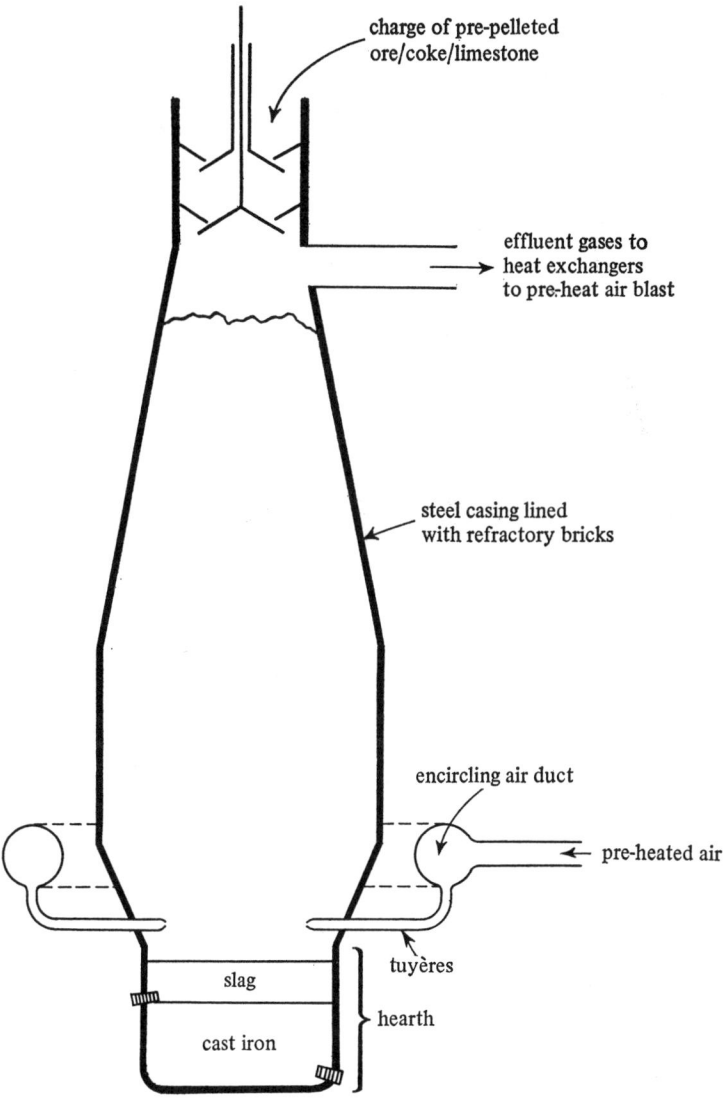

charge of pre-pelleted
ore/coke/limestone

effluent gases to
heat exchangers
to pre-heat air blast

steel casing lined
with refractory bricks

encircling air duct

pre-heated air

tuyères

slag

cast iron

hearth

Blast furnace.

This slag collects on the top of the molten iron. In the absence of limestone the furnace would quickly become choked and prevent continuous functioning.

Effluent gases are hot and contain considerable quantities of combustible carbon monoxide and these are used to preheat the air blast.

Slag and cast iron are tapped off separately. Most of the iron is transported immediately to the steelmaking plant.

Properties and uses of cast iron

Contains 4–5% carbon and, usually, small quantities of P, S, Si, Mn. The solid is brittle and very hard. It is useless for structural purposes but good for the production of heavy cast objects (grates, drainpipes, etc.).

CONVERSION OF CAST IRON TO STEEL

A steel is an alloy of iron, containing small quantities of carbon ($\frac{1}{2}\%$ in mild steel, 1·5% in hard steel) and often other metals—usually transition metals, e.g. Cr, Mn, W.

There are two principal steelmaking processes:

(a) The Open Hearth process
(b) The Bessemer process

and each may have two modifications:

(i) *A basic process:* furnace lining is calcined dolomite (CaO,MgO) and limestone is added to the charge; this is used when the cast iron from the blast furnace contains phosphorus; most steel in the UK is made by this method.

(ii) *An acid process:* furnace lining is of silica and this process is used when phosphorus is absent.

(a) Open Hearth process

The dissolved impurities are oxidised by the iron oxide and by the air, e.g.

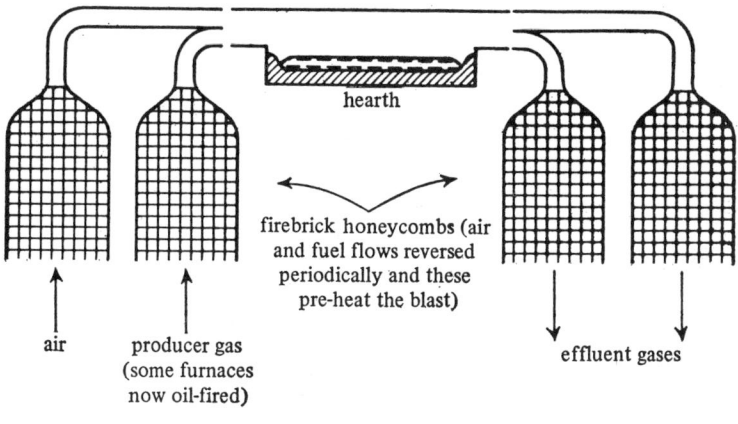

$$Fe_2O_3 + 3C \longrightarrow 2Fe + 3CO$$
$$2Fe_2O_3 + 3Si \longrightarrow 4Fe + 3SiO_2$$

Quicklime (from dissociation of added limestone) reacts with the oxides of silicon and phosphorus forming a fusible slag of calcium silicate and phosphate. Some reaction also occurs with the lining.

The addition of alloying elements and any carbon adjustment is made towards the end of the process.

(b) Bessemer process

The silicon and manganese oxidise, producing much heat (enough for external heating to be unnecessary). The carbon forms CO which burns at the converter mouth; when the flame suddenly dies away all the carbon has been removed (20 min approx.). Blowing is continued for 2–3 min to oxidise all the phosphorus, which forms a calcium phosphate slag. Finally ferromanganese (a Fe/Mn/C alloy) is added. The manganese reduces iron oxides formed in the process and the manganese oxide passes into the slag; the carbon in the alloy brings its percentage to the required level.

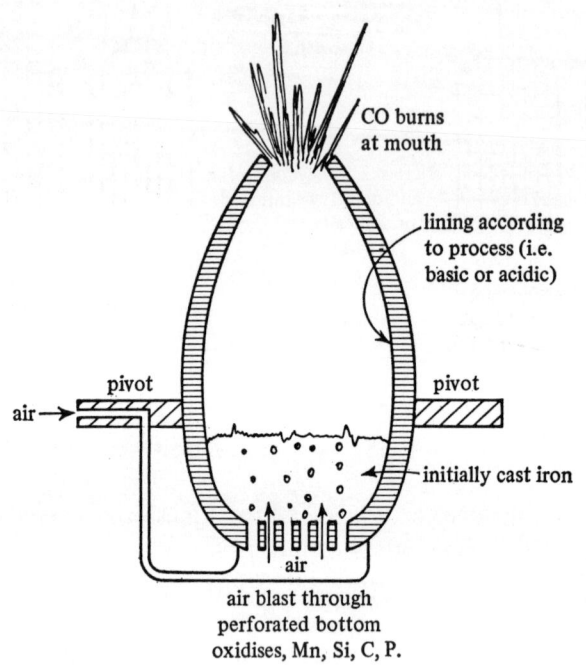

CO burns
at mouth

lining according
to process (i.e.
basic or acidic)

pivot

pivot

air →

initially cast iron

air

air blast through
perforated bottom
oxidises, Mn, Si, C, P.

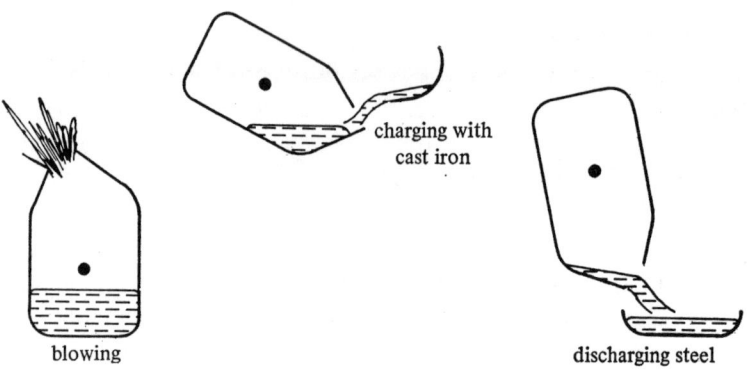

charging with
cast iron

blowing

discharging steel

An important modification of the Bessemer process is the
L.D. (Linz–Donawitz) process. In this the bottom of the converter is not perforated, and oxidation of impurities is effected
by pure oxygen introduced from the top via a water-cooled
lance. *The L.D. process has now almost completely replaced the
Open Hearth and Bessemer processes.*

ZINC

Sources: calamine ($ZnCO_3$), blende (ZnS) which often occurs
with galena (PbS) from which it is separated by flotation.

(1) **Thermal process**
The ores are heated in air

$$2ZnS + 3O_2 \longrightarrow 2ZnO + 2SO_2$$
$$ZnCO_3 \longrightarrow ZnO + CO_2$$

The oxide is charged, with excess coke, into a blast furnace
where reduction occurs

$$ZnO + CO \longrightarrow Zn + CO_2$$
$$ZnO + C \longrightarrow Zn + CO$$

Zinc vapour (b.p. Zn 910°C) issues from the top of the furnace
with CO and CO_2 and is cooled by molten lead, in which it
dissolves after condensing. Cooling the lead/zinc mixture
slightly yields an upper layer of molten zinc which is tapped
off. The zinc (containing 2% lead) is purified by distillation
(b.p. Pb 1600°C).

(2) Electrolytic process

Blende is gently roasted in air

$$ZnS + 2O_2 \longrightarrow ZnSO_4$$

and the product is leached with dilute sulphuric acid to yield an impure zinc sulphate solution.

A little milk of lime is added to precipitate iron and aluminium

$$Fe^{3+} + 3OH^- \longrightarrow Fe(OH)_3 \downarrow \; ;$$
$$Al^{3+} + 3OH^- \longrightarrow Al(OH)_3 \downarrow$$

and then zinc dust is added to precipitate the less electropositive metals copper and cadmium

$$Cu^{2+} + Zn \longrightarrow Cu \downarrow + Zn^{2+} ;$$
$$Cd^{2+} + Zn \longrightarrow Cd \downarrow + Zn^{2+}$$

The resulting pure zinc sulphate solution is acidified and then electrolysed in the cell

$$\underset{\text{(anode)}}{Pb} \Big| \underset{\text{(aqueous)}}{ZnSO_4} \Big| \underset{\text{(cathode)}}{Al}$$

At anode: $4OH^- - 4e \longrightarrow 2H_2O + O_2 \uparrow$ (overall equation)

At cathode: $Zn^{2+} + 2e \longrightarrow Zn$

The pure zinc is then stripped from the aluminium cathodes.

TIN

Source: tinstone or cassiterite (SnO_2)

Extraction

The prepared ore is roasted in air to remove sulphur and arsenic as their oxides.

The tin(IV) oxide is then heated with coal, when reduction

occurs, and the liquid metal is run off from the bottom of the furnace

$$SnO_2 + 2C \longrightarrow Sn + 2CO$$

The tin is purified from iron and other metals by heating on an inclined hearth. The low m.p. tin (232°C) melts and runs down the hearth, leaving behind the other metals.

LEAD

Sources: galena (PbS) often in association with blende (ZnS); cerussite (PbCO$_3$); anglesite (PbSO$_4$)

Extraction

The prepared galena (principal ore) is partially converted to lead(II) oxide and sulphate by roasting in air

$$2PbS + 3O_2 \longrightarrow 2PbO + 2SO_2$$
$$PbS + 2O_2 \longrightarrow PbSO_4$$

The air supply is cut off and the temperature raised; auto-reduction then occurs

$$PbS + 2PbO \longrightarrow 3Pb + SO_2$$
$$PbS + PbSO_4 \longrightarrow 2Pb + 2SO_2$$

Purification is by electrolysis using impure lead anodes, pure lead cathodes and an electrolyte of lead(II) hexafluorosilicate dissolved in hexafluorosilicic acid.

At anode: $(Pb \longrightarrow Pb^{2+} + 2e)$

At cathode: $Pb^{2+} + 2e \longrightarrow Pb$

Impurities (Cu, Bi, Ag, Au) deposit as a sludge on the bottom of the cell and this is worked for the last three valuable metals.

COPPER

Sources: copper pyrites $(CuFeS_2)$; malachite $(CuCO_3,Cu(OH)_2)$; azurite $(2CuCO_3,Cu(OH)_2)$. Some copper occurs native in Canada.

Extraction from copper pyrites

The concentrated ore is roasted gently in air, when the more readily oxidised iron (above Cu in E.C.S.) is converted to iron(II) oxide

$$2CuFeS_2 + 4O_2 \longrightarrow 2FeO + 3SO_2 + Cu_2S$$

On stronger heating the iron(II) oxide forms a molten silicate slag (with earthy materials in the ore)

$$FeO + SiO_2 \longrightarrow FeSiO_3$$

and this floats on a lower layer of fused copper(I) sulphide. The layers are separated.

The crude copper(I) sulphide is subjected to an air blast, when partial oxidation occurs

$$2Cu_2S + 3O_2 \longrightarrow 2Cu_2O + 2SO_2$$

The air blast is shut off and on raising the temperature auto-reduction occurs

$$Cu_2S + 2Cu_2O \longrightarrow 6Cu + SO_2$$

The reactions are highly exothermic and the temperature rises to about 2400°C.

Purification is by electrolysis using impure copper anodes, pure copper cathodes and an electrolyte of aqueous copper(II) sulphate

At anode: $Cu \longrightarrow Cu^{2+} + 2e$
At cathode: $Cu^{2+} + 2e \longrightarrow Cu$

MERCURY

Source: cinnabar (HgS)

Extraction—there are two methods

1. by roasting the ore in air

$$HgS + O_2 \longrightarrow Hg + SO_2$$

2. by heating the ore with iron filings

$$HgS + Fe \longrightarrow Hg + FeS$$

In both cases the mercury is obtained as vapour which is condensed in water-cooled pipes. The element is purified by distillation at low pressure.

SILVER

Sources: argentite or silver glance (Ag_2S); horn silver (AgCl). Both are low grade ores containing 1–2% silver.

The cyanide process

Argentite ore is agitated with aqueous sodium cyanide by blowing air through the mixture

$$Ag_2S + 4CN^- \rightleftharpoons 2[Ag(CN)_2]^- + S^{2-} \qquad (1)$$

$$S^{2-} + 2O_2 \longrightarrow SO_4^{2-} \qquad (2)$$

Removal of S^{2-} ions by reaction (2) causes almost quantitative displacement of (1) to the right.

Horn silver does not require air

$$AgCl + 2CN^- \longrightarrow [Ag(CN)_2]^- + Cl^-$$

Zinc is then added when the less electropositive silver is displaced

$$[Ag(CN)_2]^- \rightleftharpoons Ag^+ + 2CN^-$$
$$Zn + 2Ag^+ \longrightarrow Zn^{2+} + 2Ag$$

and $$Zn^{2+} + 4CN^- \rightleftharpoons [Zn(CN)_4]^{2-}$$

SECTION B: THE NON-METALS

EXTRACTION METHODS

In contrast to the metals the non-metals are sometimes isolated by oxidation processes, as is the case with the halogens F, Cl and Br when uninegative halide ions are converted to the free halogen

$$Cl^- - e \longrightarrow Cl; \quad 2Cl \longrightarrow Cl_2 \text{ (at an anode)}$$
$$2Br^- + Cl_2 \longrightarrow Br_2 + 2Cl^-$$

Some common non-metals, e.g. S, O, N (and to some small extent C) occur native, and so chemical processes are not involved in their extraction. On the other hand, several of the less electronegative elements which occur as oxides or in oxyanions are obtained by reduction methods, e.g. P, Si, As, H.

$$4PO_4^{3-} + 6SiO_2 + 10C \longrightarrow 6SiO_3^{2-} + P_4 + 10CO$$

HYDROGEN

Sources: principally water and petroleum; to some extent coal

Extraction

1. *From water gas (Bosch process)*
Water gas, which is manufactured by passing steam through white hot coke (see p. 121)

$$C + H_2O \rightleftharpoons CO + H_2$$

is mixed with excess steam and passed over an activated iron(III) oxide catalyst at normal pressures when more hydrogen is produced by reduction of the steam. (See *Revision Notes for Advanced Level Physical Chemistry*, p. 51, for the physico-chemical principle.)

$$CO + H_2O \rightleftharpoons CO + H_2$$

The carbon dioxide is removed by dissolving it in water under pressure and the last traces of carbon monoxide (a catalyst poison) by an ammoniacal solution of copper(I) chloride (forms CuCl,CO).

2. By-product in the manufacture of chlorine and sodium hydroxide

The sodium amalgam from the Kellner–Solvay cell (see p. 123), when reacted with water, yields a quantity of hydrogen equivalent to the chlorine liberated during the electrolysis of the brine

$$2Na + 2H_2O \longrightarrow 2NaOH + H_2$$

3. From petroleum

High M.W. alkanes when raised to high temperatures in the presence of catalysts (e.g. SiO_2/Al_2O_3) yield hydrocarbons of low M.W. and considerable quantities of hydrogen. This process is called 'cracking'. The hydrogen is separated by fractional condensation.

CARBON

Sources: occurs native as diamond and graphite; coal

Artificial graphite from coke (Acheson process)

Coke (or charcoal) and sand are heated together in an electric furnace. It is thought that silicon carbide (carborundum) is produced and that this then dissociates to give vapours of Si and C—the former escaping but the latter rapidly condensing to graphite.

$$SiO_2 + 3C \longrightarrow SiC + 2CO$$
$$SiC \rightleftharpoons Si + C$$

NITROGEN AND OXYGEN

Source: air

Separation

This is effected by the fractional distillation of liquid air (a mixture of liquid nitrogen, b.p. $-196°C$, and liquid oxygen, b.p. $-183°C$). Nitrogen being the more volatile is collected from the top of the fractionation column, while oxygen runs back. No constant b.p. mixture (azeotropic mixture) is formed and so complete separation is possible (see *Revision Notes for Advanced Level Physical Chemistry*, p. 97).

PHOSPHORUS

Source: phosphate rock (fluorapatite), $CaF_2,3Ca_3(PO_4)_2$

Extraction

Phosphate rock is heated in air to sinter (i.e. make granular) when about half of the fluorine is removed—probably as SiF_4.

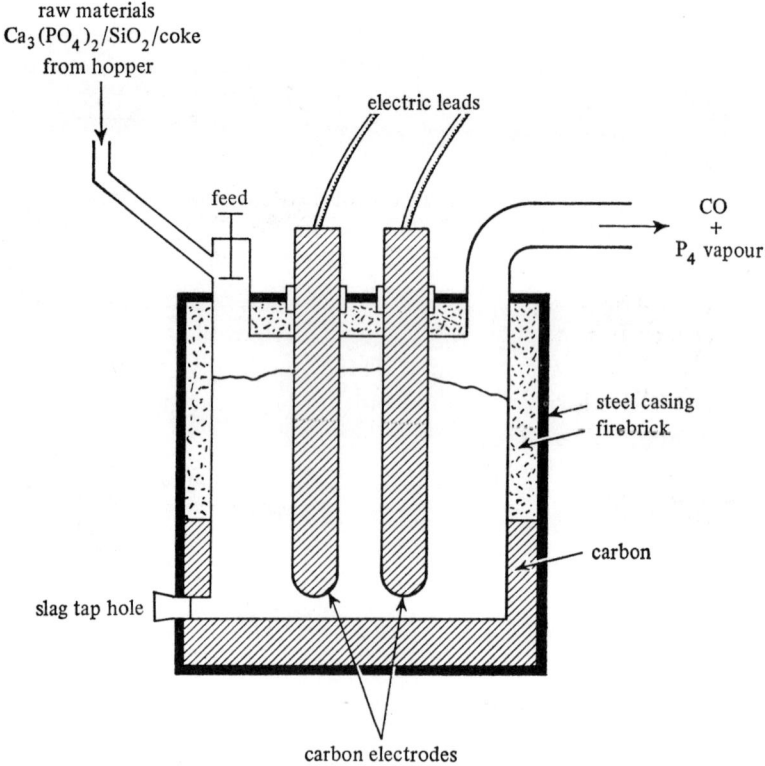

raw materials
$Ca_3(PO_4)_2/SiO_2/coke$
from hopper

electric leads

feed

CO
+
P_4 vapour

steel casing
firebrick

carbon

slag tap hole

carbon electrodes

The prepared mineral, sand and coke are fed into an electric furnace whose temperature is approx. 1500°C; the phosphate is reduced to phosphorus

$$2Ca_3(PO_4)_2 + 6SiO_2 + 10C \longrightarrow 6CaSiO_3 + P_4 + 10CO$$

which emerges as vapour, mixed with carbon monoxide, and is condensed to a liquid by sprays of warm water. The liquid is collected under warm water and either allowed to cool and solidify as yellow (white) phosphorus or converted to the stable red allotrope. The calcium silicate forms a liquid slag which is tapped off periodically.

Conversion to red phosphorus

The liquid yellow phosphorus is heated to 270°C for 4–5 days in a steel pot and with exclusion of air; most of the phosphorus is converted. The temperature is then raised to 400°C to distil off unchanged yellow phosphorus, and then any final traces of this allotrope are removed by boiling with aqueous sodium carbonate

$$CO_3^{2-} + H_2O \rightleftharpoons CO_2 + 2OH^-$$
$$3OH^- + P_4 + 3H_2O \longrightarrow 3H_2PO_2^- + PH_3$$

The red phosphorus is washed, filtered off and dried in vacuo.

SULPHUR

Source: native sulphur, e.g. in Sicily, Texas, Louisiana

Extraction: the Frasch Process (USA)

The native sulphur beds lie beneath quicksand, ruling out conventional mining methods.

A complex of three concentric tubes is lowered through a borehole. Superheated water (170–180°C) is pumped down the outer tube—this melts the sulphur (m.p. 120°C) and also provides a hot outer jacket. Compressed air is passed down the inner tube and this forces a mixture of water and molten sulphur

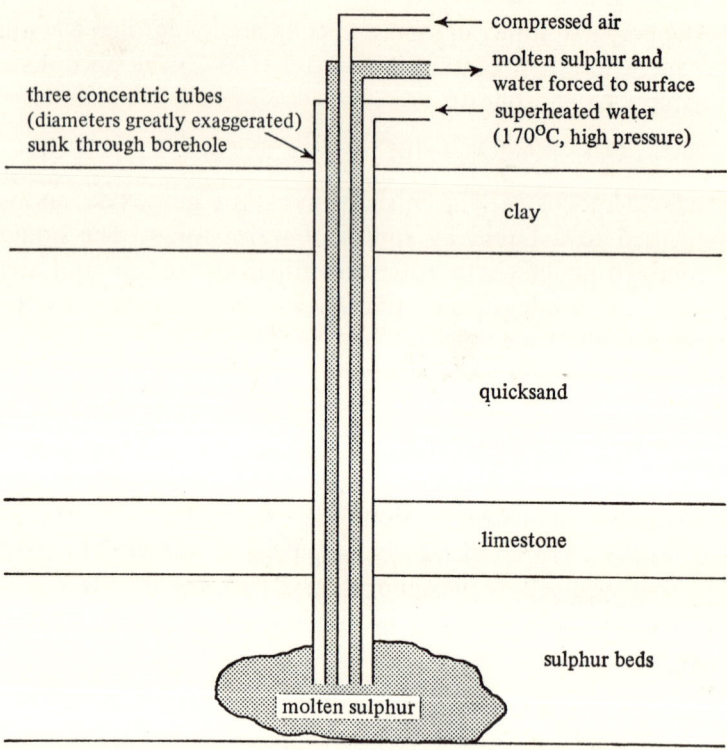

to the surface via the remaining tube. The mixture is run into wooden vats when the sulphur solidifies. It is over 99·8% pure.

FLUORINE

Source: fluorspar (CaF_2)

Extraction

Anhydrous hydrofluoric acid is made by distilling 99% sulphuric acid with fluorspar and the vapours are condensed to the liquid (b.p. 19·4°C)

$$CaF_2 + H_2SO_4 \longrightarrow CaSO_4 + 2HF$$

This acid is used to make potassium hydrogen fluoride (KHF_2)

by treatment with potassium hydroxide in the requisite proportion followed by crystallisation.

$$HF + OH^- \longrightarrow F^- + H_2O; \qquad F^- + HF \longrightarrow HF_2^-$$

Fluorine is then obtained by electrolysing an equimolar mixture of KHF_2 and HF at between 80°C and 100°C, the electrolyte having a m.p. of 70°C.

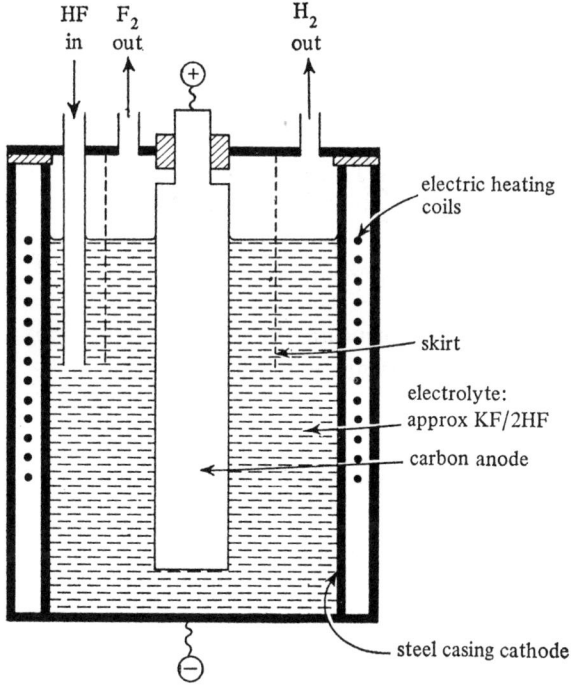

Reaction at cathode:

$$H^+ + e \longrightarrow H; \qquad H + H \longrightarrow H_2$$

Reaction at anode:

$$F^- - e \longrightarrow F; \qquad F + F \longrightarrow F_2$$

The fluorine is freed from hydrogen fluoride by reaction with potassium fluoride

$$F^- + HF \longrightarrow HF_2^-$$

CHLORINE

Source: principally rock salt (NaCl)

Extraction

Chlorine and caustic soda are produced by the same industrial process, and this is dealt with on p. 122.

The demand for chlorine, however, is tending to exceed that for sodium hydroxide and some is now being recovered from HCl, which is a by-product from the manufacture of chlorinated hydrocarbons. The hydrogen chloride is oxidised by air in the presence of a heated copper(II) chloride catalyst

$$4HCl + O_2 \rightleftharpoons 2Cl_2 + 2H_2O$$

Other sources of chlorine are the electrolyses of fused chlorides in the extraction of metals, e.g. Na, Mg.

BROMINE

Sources: Br^- ions in sea water (ca. 0·04%); salt deposits, e.g. Stassfurt

Extraction

1. *From sea water*

This is acidified and chlorinated. A very dilute aqueous solution of bromine is formed

$$2Br^- + Cl_2 \longrightarrow Br_2 + 2Cl^-$$

and the presence of hydrogen ions from the acid minimises the extensive hydrolysis in this very dilute solution by forcing the equilibrium to the left

$$Br_2 + H_2O \rightleftharpoons 2H^+ + OBr^- + Br^-$$

Air is then blown through the solution to vaporise the bromine, and the vapour is absorbed in sodium carbonate solution

$$3Br_2 + 3CO_3^{2-} \longrightarrow 5Br^- + BrO_3^- + 3CO_2$$

This bromide/bromate solution is then acidified, when bromine separates as a lower layer

$$5Br^- + BrO_3^- + 6H^+ \longrightarrow 3Br_2 + 3H_2O$$

The bromine is purified from chlorine by distilling over solid potassium bromide

$$2Br^- + Cl_2 \longrightarrow Br_2 + 2Cl^-$$

2. From salt deposits

Solutions prepared from bromide-rich salt deposits (almost invariably predominantly chlorides) are fractionally crystallised. The less soluble chlorides crystallise first, and the mother liquor is treated with chlorine and steam. Bromine is displaced and vaporises in the steam

$$2Br^- + Cl_2 \longrightarrow Br_2 + 2Cl^-$$

Condensation yields a two-layer system of bromine/water. The lower bromine layer is separated and purified from chlorine by distilling over potassium bromide.

IODINE

Source: principally the Chilean salt deposits of 'caliche'—mainly $NaNO_3$ with a small percentage of $NaIO_3$.

Extraction

The mother liquor, after crystallising out sodium nitrate, contains about $3 g dm^{-3}$ of iodine as iodate. This iodate solution is treated with sulphur dioxide, when reduction to iodide occurs

$$IO_3^- + 3SO_2 + 3H_2O \longrightarrow I^- + 3SO_4^{2-} + 6H^+$$

Addition of more iodate results in the liberation of iodine as a fine suspension

$$IO_3^- + 5I^- + 6H^+ \longrightarrow 3I_2 + 3H_2O$$

Solid iodine is obtained from the suspension by a flotation method. The froth/iodine mixture obtained is heated under pressure when the iodine melts and forms a lower layer. This is tapped off and allowed to solidify.

Chapter 8

The Manufacture of Some Commercially Important Compounds

(1) FUEL GASES

(*a*) **Producer gas and water gas**

These are always manufactured with the same plant—by blowing air and steam alternately through hot coke.

The air blast (coke at 1000°C) yields producer gas by an exothermic reaction

$$2C + O_2 \rightleftharpoons 2CO$$

The steam blast (commenced when the coke temperature exceeds 1100°C) yields water gas by an endothermic reaction

$$C + H_2O \rightleftharpoons CO + H_2$$

As the coke cools below 1000°C the equilibrium swings to the left (Le Châtelier's Principle) and is slow to be established—the air blast is restarted.

Producer gas is cheap but approx. 65% of its volume is incombustible nitrogen. Its calorific value is low. It is usually burned immediately, before its temperature falls and much heat is lost.

Water gas (49% H_2, 44% CO, 3% CO_2 and 4% N_2 approx.) has a high calorific value since (i) it is nearly all combustible and (ii) it contains hydrogen which has a very high heat of combustion.

121

(b) Coal gas

COAL——→
(heated in
absence of
air)

{

GAS — impure coal gas containing 50% H_2, 30% CH_4, 8% CO and small percentages of N_2, NH_3, SO_2, H_2S, H_2O and higher hydrocarbons

LIQUID — two-layer condensate
(i) black lower layer—coal tar—source of organic chemicals
(ii) upper aqueous layer— soln. of ammonia—used to manufacture $(NH_4)_2SO_4$ fertiliser

COKE — residue

The gaseous product is washed with water (to remove NH_3, SO_2 and residual tar) and then passed over moist iron(III) oxide, which removes H_2S

$$Fe_2O_3 + 3H_2S \longrightarrow Fe_2S_3 + 3H_2O$$

and traces of cyanogen ($(CN)_2$) and HCN (as cyanides of iron). The oxide is regenerated by exposure to air

$$2Fe_2S_3 + 3O_2 \longrightarrow 2Fe_2O_3 + 6S$$

and is re-used until the sulphur content is high; the sulphur is then burned off to yield SO_2 for sulphuric acid manufacture.

(2) SODIUM COMPOUNDS

(a) Sodium hydroxide (caustic soda, NaOH)

The Kellner–Solvay Process

During electrolysis Cl^- ions are discharged at the carbon anodes in preference to OH^- ions since the former are in high

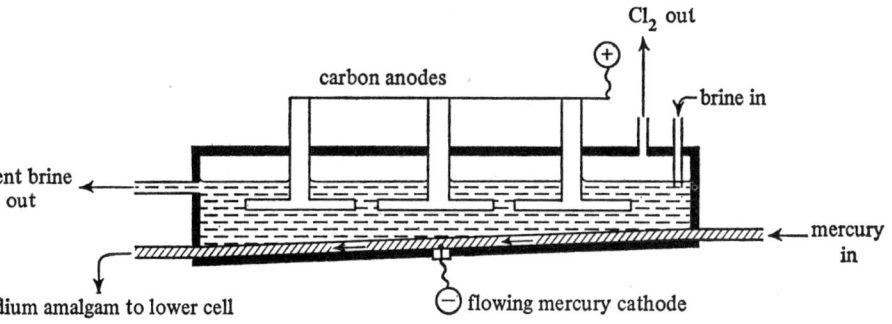

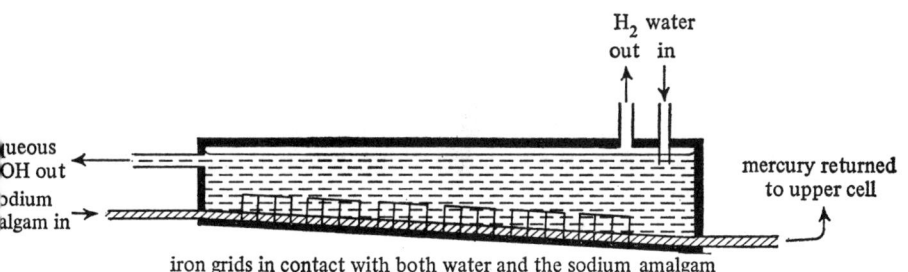

iron grids in contact with both water and the sodium amalgam

concentration (see *Revision Notes for Advanced Level Physical Chemistry*, chapter 12)

$$Cl^- - e \longrightarrow Cl; \qquad Cl + Cl \longrightarrow Cl_2$$

and this, in fact, is the major source of chlorine.

At the flowing mercury cathode sodium ions are discharged in preference to the H^+ ions despite the relative positions of these in the E.C.S. (see p. 11). This is because of the high overpotential required for the discharge of H^+ at a mercury electrode.

$$Na^+ + e \longrightarrow Na$$

The liberated sodium dissolves in the mercury to give an amalgam. The amalgam is passed to another vessel where it is brought into contact with water and iron grids; a galvanic cell is produced

$$\text{Na/Hg} \mid \begin{array}{c} \text{-----------in contact-----------} \\ \text{water} \\ H_2O \rightleftharpoons H^+ + OH^- \end{array} \mid \text{Fe}$$
$$\text{anode} \qquad\qquad\qquad\qquad\qquad\qquad \text{cathode}$$

and sodium passes into solution as ions

$$Na - e \longrightarrow Na^+$$

while H^+ ions (from water) are discharged at the iron cathode

$$H^+ + e \longrightarrow H; \qquad H + H \longrightarrow H_2$$

This leaves OH^- ions (from water) in solution with Na^+ ions and evaporation leaves molten caustic soda which solidifies on cooling.

The mercury is returned to the upper cell.

Brine must flow through the Kellner–Solvay cell at such a rate that the Cl^- concentration does not fall below a certain level. Should this occur OH^- ions may be discharged and the chlorine is polluted with oxygen.

(b) Sodium carbonate and sodium hydrogen carbonate

The Solvay (or ammonia–soda) Process

Concentrated brine is saturated with ammonia and passed down a tower up which carbon dioxide is bubbled.

Carbon dioxide reacts with water to yield carbonic acid which is weakly dissociated

$$H_2CO_3 \rightleftharpoons H^+ + HCO_3^- \rightleftharpoons 2H^+ + CO_3^{2-}$$

The dissociation to yield hydrogen carbonate (and to a much lesser extent, carbonate) ions is assisted by the removal of H^+ ions by ammonia

$$NH_3 + H^+ \longrightarrow NH_4^+$$

Sodium hydrogen carbonate is not very soluble in water and much less so in brine (common ion effect); hence it precipitates

$$Na^+ + HCO_3^- \longrightarrow NaHCO_3 \downarrow$$

The effluent from the tower is a sludge of $NaHCO_3$ in a solution containing NH_4^+ and Cl^- ions (i.e. ammonium chloride). The suspension is filtered to yield solid **sodium hydrogen carbonate**. (N.B. $KHCO_3$ is much more soluble and cannot be prepared by a similar process.)

The **hydrogen carbonate** is heated to give **anhydrous sodium carbonate** (or **soda ash**) and carbon dioxide

$$2NaHCO_3 \longrightarrow Na_2CO_3 + CO_2 + H_2O$$
i.e. $\qquad 2HCO_3^- \longrightarrow CO_3^{2-} + CO_2 + H_2O$

the carbon dioxide being recirculated.

To obtain **washing soda** ($Na_2CO_3,10H_2O$) the anhydrous salt is dissolved in hot water and crystallised.

Carbon dioxide for the process is obtained from limestone

$$CaCO_3 \rightleftharpoons CaO + CO_2$$

and the quicklime is slaked and used to recover ammonia from the ammonium chloride solution after filtration

$$NH_4^+ + OH^- \longrightarrow NH_3 + H_2O$$

The only waste product is calcium chloride—there is little demand for this.

(*c*) **Sodium hypochlorite and chlorate**—see pp. 130 and 131

(3) CALCIUM COMPOUNDS

(*a*) **Calcium oxide (quicklime, CaO) and hydroxide (slaked lime, Ca(OH)₂)**

A lime kiln is a tall brickwork tower into the top of which is introduced a mixture of limestone ($CaCO_3$) and coal. A draught of air passes through the charge and combustion of the coal generates sufficient heat to effect the dissociation of the lime-stone

$$CaCO_3 \rightleftharpoons CaO + CO_2$$

The CO_2 is removed by the airstream and so equilibrium is not established (see *Revision Notes for Advanced Level Physical Chemistry*, p. 53).

Some kilns are heated by producer gas and, in these cases, coal does not form part of the charge.

Slaked lime is produced by treating the quicklime with water

$$CaO + H_2O \longrightarrow Ca(OH)_2$$

The reaction is highly exothermic.

(b) Calcium carbide

Quicklime and coke are heated in an electric furnace (temperature approx. 2000°C)

$$CaO + 3C \longrightarrow CaC_2 + CO$$

and the molten carbide is tapped off periodically and allowed to solidify. It is used in the manufacture of calcium cyanamide (below) and acetylene (ethyne)

$$C_2^{2-} + 2H_2O \longrightarrow 2OH^- + C_2H_2 \uparrow$$

(c) Calcium cyanamide

Calcium carbide is heated in nitrogen at 1200°C

$$CaC_2 + N_2 \longrightarrow CaCN_2 + C$$
i.e. $\quad\quad C_2^{2-} + N_2 \longrightarrow CN_2^{2-} + C$

It is used as a fertiliser—being slowly hydrolysed to ammonia

$$CN_2^{2-} + 3H_2O \longrightarrow CO_3^{2-} + 2NH_3$$

(d) Calcium 'superphosphate'—see p. 128

(e) Bleaching powder—see p. 132

(4) NITROGEN COMPOUNDS

(a) Ammonia (NH_3)

The Haber Process

Hydrogen and nitrogen (for manufactures see pp. 112 and 113) in volume ratio 3:1 and at a pressure of 200 atm are passed over a catalyst (iron, containing an Al_2O_3 promoter) at about 550°C. About 10% conversion to ammonia is effected. The issuing gas mixture is refrigerated, when the ammonia liquefies. Unconverted gas is replenished and re-circulated.

$$N_2 + 3H_2 \rightleftharpoons 2NH_3$$

The system is exothermic to the right. For the physico-chemical principles see p. 54 of *Revision Notes for Advanced Level Physical Chemistry*.

(b) Nitric acid (HNO_3)

A preheated, dust-free mixture of air and ammonia is passed through a platinum/rhodium gauze catalyst maintained at about 900°C (the catalyst is heated initially but thereafter is maintained at the required temperature by the exothermic reaction and control of the gas flow rate)

$$4NH_3 + 5O_2 \rightleftharpoons 4NO + 6H_2O$$

Over 95% of the ammonia is oxidised to nitrogen monoxide.

The issuing gases are cooled and mixed with more air; further oxidation occurs to nitrogen dioxide

$$2NO + O_2 \rightleftharpoons 2NO_2$$

(cooling is essential, otherwise this equilibrium lies to the left). Absorption of the nitrogen dioxide in water yields nitrous and nitric acids, but the former rapidly decompose

$$2NO_2 + H_2O \longrightarrow HNO_2 + HNO_3$$
$$3HNO_2 \longrightarrow HNO_3 + 2NO + H_2O$$

and this nitrogen monoxide is converted to nitrogen dioxide by air.

The nitric acid produced by this process is about 60% concentration. Fractional distillation yields a maximum constant b.p. mixture (68%), and from this may be made 98% acid by distillation with concentrated sulphuric acid.

(c) **Calcium cyanamide**—see p. 126

(5) PHOSPHORUS COMPOUNDS

(a) **Orthophosphoric acid (H_3PO_4)**

(i) Yellow phosphorus is burned in excess dry air

$$P_4 + 5O_2 \longrightarrow P_4O_{10}$$

and the pentoxide is dissolved in aqueous orthophosphoric acid (rather than water, since the hydration is very vigorous) to give the concentrated ('syrupy') acid

$$P_4O_{10} + 6H_2O \longrightarrow 4H_3PO_4$$

(ii) An impure, but cheaper, acid is made by treating phosphate rock with 65% H_2SO_4 in the quantities indicated by the equation

$$Ca_3(PO_4)_2 + 3H_2SO_4 \longrightarrow 3CaSO_4 + 2H_3PO_4$$

The calcium sulphate is filtered off and the filtrate concentrated by gentle heating.

(b) **Calcium superphosphate ($Ca(H_2PO_4)_2$)**

Phosphate rock is insufficiently soluble in water to be a really effective fertiliser. It is treated with 65% H_2SO_4 in the quantities indicated by the equation, when a more soluble acid phosphate of calcium is formed (together with calcium sulphate)

$$Ca_3(PO_4)_2 + 2H_2SO_4 \longrightarrow Ca(H_2PO_4)_2 + 2CaSO_4$$

The solid products of this reaction constitute the fertiliser 'superphosphate'.

(6) SULPHUR COMPOUNDS

(a) **Sulphur dioxide (SO$_2$)**

There are several starting materials:

(i) Sulphur is burned in air

$$S + O_2 \longrightarrow SO_2$$

The gas is free from reactive impurities but is diluted with nitrogen.

(ii) Iron pyrites is heated in air

$$4FeS_2 + 11O_2 \longrightarrow 2Fe_2O_3 + 8SO_2$$

The sulphur dioxide usually contains arsenic(III) oxide (As$_2$O$_3$), a catalyst poison, which must be removed if the gas is to be used in the Contact Process.

(iii) 'Spent oxide' is heated in air—see coal gas p. 122

(iv) From anhydrite (CaSO$_4$). This is heated with carbon and silica at 1450°C

$$CaSO_4 + 4C \longrightarrow CaS + 4CO$$
then $$CaS + CaSO_4 \rightleftharpoons 2CaO + 2SO_2 \qquad \text{(i)}$$
but $$CaO + SiO_2 \longrightarrow CaSiO_3$$

i.e. equilibrium (i) is not established since CaO is removed by the silica.

(v) Small, but valuable, quantities are obtained during some metal extraction processes, e.g. Cu, Pb, Zn (see Chapter 7).

(b) **Sulphuric acid (H$_2$SO$_4$)**

The Contact Process

Purified sulphur dioxide (for manufacture see above) mixed with excess air and preheated to 450°C is passed through converters containing a vanadium(V) oxide (V$_2$O$_5$) catalyst. 96% conversion of the sulphur dioxide is achieved.

$$2SO_2 + O_2 \rightleftharpoons 2SO_3$$

The reaction is exothermic to the right, and the optimum conditions for maximum conversion may be predicted by applying Le Châtelier's Principle (see *Revision Notes for Advanced Level Physical Chemistry*, p. 54). High pressures are not used because the percentage conversion is very high at ordinary pressures.

The SO_3 formed is then absorbed in concentrated sulphuric acid which is continuously diluted with water to maintain the concentration at 98%

$$SO_3 + H_2O \longrightarrow H_2SO_4$$

The direct absorption of SO_3 in water is not employed since acid mist, which cannot be condensed, is formed during the highly exothermic reaction.

If SO_3 is absorbed in conc. sulphuric acid without the addition of water a solution of sulphur trioxide in anhydrous sulphuric acid is obtained. This is oleum or fuming sulphuric acid. It is an important reagent in the manufacture of organic chemicals, particularly detergents.

(7) CHLORINE COMPOUNDS

(*a*) **Sodium hypochlorite (NaOCl)**

This important bleaching agent and disinfectant is manufactured by passing chlorine into aqueous sodium hydroxide

$$2NaOH + Cl_2 \longrightarrow NaCl + NaOCl + H_2O$$
or $\quad\; 2OH^- + Cl_2 \longrightarrow Cl^- + OCl^- + H_2O$

Some is manufactured by electrolysing cold brine in such a way that the products of electrolysis interact in the cell:

Ions present: Na^+, Cl^-, H^+, OH^-
(latter two from $H_2O \rightleftharpoons H^+ + OH^-$)

Reaction at cathode: H^+ ions preferentially discharged (see relative positions of Na and H in E.C.S., p. 11)

$$H^+ + e \longrightarrow H; \quad H + H \longrightarrow H_2$$

This disturbs the water ionisation equilibrium and the solution becomes progressively more alkaline as OH^- ions accumulate. *Reaction at anode:* Cl^- ions preferentially discharged (concentration effect)

$$Cl^- - e \longrightarrow Cl; \quad Cl + Cl \longrightarrow Cl_2$$

The elementary chlorine and the OH^- ions yield chloride and hypochlorite

$$Cl_2 + 2OH^- \longrightarrow Cl^- + OCl^- + H_2O$$

The Cl^- ions are discharged again, in preference to both OH^- and OCl^- ions. The effluent solution contains primarily Na^+ and OCl^- ions (i.e. aqueous sodium hypochlorite). It is used in this form.

(b) Sodium chlorate ($NaClO_3$)

The manufacture of this compound is essentially the same as for the hypochlorite. The principal differences being (a) the electrolyte is made slightly acid (N.B. there are still OH^- ions present—see *ionic product of water*, p. 64 of *Revision Notes for Advanced Level Physical Chemistry*) and (b) cooling is unnecessary; indeed higher temperatures help chlorate formation.

In the presence of acid the formation of free hypochlorous acid is favoured

$$H^+ + OCl^- \rightleftharpoons HOCl$$

and this hypochlorous acid interacts with more hypochlorite ions to give chlorate ions

$$OCl^- + 2HOCl \longrightarrow 2Cl^- + ClO_3^- + 2H^+$$

The effluent solution is concentrated by heating and the salt is crystallised. It is an important weedkiller.

Potassium chlorate is very much less soluble than the sodium salt. It is manufactured by mixing aqueous KCl and $NaClO_3$ followed by fractional crystallisation.

(c) Bleaching powder

This is manufactured by bringing chlorine into intimate contact with slaked lime in water-cooled towers, the cooling minimising the formation of chlorate. The reaction may be represented

$$Cl_2 + Ca(OH)_2 \longrightarrow Ca(OCl)Cl + H_2O$$

but $Ca(OCl)Cl$ is an oversimplified formula. The powder is a mixture of calcium hypochlorite $Ca(OCl)_2$ and basic calcium chloride $CaCl_2,Ca(OH)_2$ together with small quantities of chlorate $Ca(ClO_3)_2$. It always contains some free slaked lime.

Index

Acheson Process, 113
Acids, 15
  nitric, 63, 127
  sulphuric, 74, 129
Acid chlorides, 27
  salts, 20
Acidic oxides, 18
Alkali metals, 37
Alkaline earth metals, 42
Allotropy, 14
  carbon, 51
  oxygen, 68
  phosphorus, 59
  tin, 51
Aluminium, 46
  extraction, 100
  flowsheet, 49
Alums, 48
Ammonia flowsheets, 62, 64
  manufacture, 127
Ammonia–Soda Process, 124
Ammonium compounds, 64
Amphoteric oxides, 19
Antimony, 58
Argon, 82
Arsenic, 58
Atomic radii, 5

Barium, 42
Bases, 16
Basic oxides, 18
  salts, 21
Basicity, 16
Bauxite, 100

Bessemer Process, 105
Bismuth, 58
Blast furnace, 103
Bleaching powder, 132
Boron, 46
Bosch Process, 112
Bromine, 75
  extraction, 118
  flowsheet, 80

Calcium, 42
  carbide, manufacture, 126
  cyanamide, manufacture, 126
  flowsheet, 45
  oxide, manufacture, 125
  'superphosphate', manufacture, 128
Carbon, 50
  allotropy, 51
  flowsheet, 54
  graphite, manufacture, 113
Carborundum, 113
Cast iron, 104
Catalysts (transition metal), 88
Chlorine, 75
  extraction, 118, 112
  flowsheet, 79
Chromium flowsheet, 89
Classification, Periodic, 1
Complex salts, 22
Compounds, types of, 13
Configurations, electronic,1 (facing)
Contact Process, 129
Co-ordination number, 23

Copper flowsheet, 92
  extraction, 110
Cryolite, 101

Decomposition, 28
Dehydration, 29
Diagonal relationships, 7
Diamond, 51
Displacement reactions, 27
Disproportionation, 27
Dissociation, 28
Dolomite, 99
Double decomposition, 29
Double salts, 22

Electrochemical series, 9
Electronic configurations, 1 (facing)
Elements, types of, 3, 13
  extractions, 96
Enantiotropy, 15

Ferrosilicon, 99
Flame colours, 42, 46
Flowsheets,
  Aluminium, 46
  Ammonia, 62, 64
  Bromine, 80
  Calcium, 45
  Carbon, 54
  Chlorine, 79
  Chromium, 89
  Copper, 92
  Hydrogen peroxide, 69
  Hydrogen sulphide, 67
  Iodine, 81
  Iron, 91
  Magnesium, 44
  Manganese, 90
  Mercury, 95
  Nitric acid, 63
  Nitrogen, 62
  Ozone, 69

Phosphorus, 68
Silicon, 55
Silver, 93
Sodium, 41
Sulphur, 70
Sulphur dioxide, 73
Sulphuric acid, 74
Tin, 56
Zinc, 94
Fluorine, 75
  extraction, 116
Frasch Process, 115

Gases,
  coal, 122
  producer, 121
  water, 121
Graphite, 51, 113
Group comparisons,
  I, 37
  II, 42
  III, 46
  IV, 50
  V, 58
  VI, 66
  VII, 75
  Noble gases, 82
  Transition elements, 85

Haber Process, 127
Halogens, 75
Helium, 83
Hydration, 29
Hydrides, 32, 34
Hydrogen, 34
  bond, 35
  carbonates, 42, 46
  extraction, 112
  fluoride, 35, 78
  peroxide, 39, 68
  sulphates, 42
  sulphide, 67, 72
Hydrolysis, 29, 48

Iodine, 75
  extraction, 119
  flowsheet, 81
Iron extraction, 102
  flowsheet, 91

Kellner–Solvay Process, 122

Lanthanides, 86
L–D Process, 107
Lead, 50
  compounds, 52, 57
  extraction, 109
  flowsheet, 57
Ligands, 23
Lime, quick, slaked, 125

Magnesium, 42
  flowsheet, 44
Manganese flowsheet, 90
Mercury flowsheet, 95
  extraction, 110
Metals, general properties, 13
  extractions, 96
Monoclinic sulphur, 68
Monotropy, 15

Nitric acid flowsheet, 63
  manufacture, 127
Nitrogen, 58
  extraction, 113
  flowsheets, 62, 63, 64
Noble gases, 82
Non-metals, general properties, 13
  extractions, 112

Open Hearth Process, 104
Orthophosphoric acid, manufacture, 128

Oxidation, 23
Oxidation number, 24
Oxide ions, 66
Oxides, 17, 67
Oxidising agents, 23
Oxygen, 66
  allotropy, 68
  extraction, 113
Ozone, 68, 69

Periodic Classification (table), 1
Peroxides, 19
Phosphoric acid, manufacture, 128
Phosphorus, 58
  allotropy, 59
  extraction, 114
  flowsheet, 68
Plastic sulphur, 68 and 75
Potassium, 37

Quicklime, 125

Reactions, types of, 12
Reactivity series, 9
Redox reactions, 27
Red phosphorus, 59, 115
Rhombic sulphur, 68

Salts, 20
  acid, 20
  basic, 21
  complex, 22
  double, 22
Silicon, 50
  flowsheet, 55
Silver, extraction, 111
  flowsheet, 93
Slaked lime, 125

Sodium, 37
    carbonate, manufacture, 124
    chlorate, manufacture, 131
    extraction, 98
    flowsheet, 41
    hydrogen carbonate, manufacture, 124
    hydroxide, manufacture, 122
    hypochlorite, manufacture, 130
Solvay Process, 124
Steel, 104
Sulphides, 67
Sulphur, 66
    allotropy, 68
    extraction, 115
    flowsheets, 70–74
Sulphur dioxide flowsheet, 73
    manufacture, 129
Sulphuric acid flowsheet, 74
    manufacture, 129

Table, Periodic, 1
Tin, 50
    allotropy, 51
    compounds, 52, 56
    extraction, 108
    flowsheet, 56
Transition metals, 85, 4

Washing soda, manufacture, 125
White phosphorus, 59, 115

Yellow phosphorus, 59, 115

Zinc flowsheet, 94
    extraction, 107